MATHEMATICS

Mechanics
Unit M3

**Professor W E Williams
& Dr S Y Barham**

AS/A LEVEL

WJEC AS/A Level Mathematics
Mechanics Unit M3

Published by the Welsh Joint Education Committee
245 Western Avenue, Cardiff, CF5 2YX

First published 2001

Printed by Hackman Printers Ltd
Clydach Vale, Tonypandy, Rhondda, CF40 2XX

ISBN: 1 86085 469 9

FOREWORD

This book covers the syllabus for the Unit M3 for the new WJEC syllabus, and also, together with the companion books M1 and M2 Mechanics, provides complete coverage of the current WJEC Mechanics syllabus. Chapter 3 also completes the coverage of the MS Unit of the syllabus.

The approach to second order differential equation in chapter 1 is relatively novel, in that, for the case when the auxilliary equation has complex roots, a justification, not involving complex numbers, is given of the method of solution.

Unfortunately, not all the errors will have been detected during the proof reading. It would be appreciated if any one coming across errors would inform the publishers so that corrections can be incorporated in subsequent editions.

CONTENTS

Chapter 1

Second Order Differential Equation

After working through this chapter you should be able

- to solve second order linear equations with constant coefficients,
- to model simple "real life" problems as second order differential equations and solve the resulting equations.

1.1 Second order linear differential equations with constant coefficients

Examples of second order linear differential equations with constant coefficients are

$$\frac{d^2x}{dt^2} + 11\frac{dx}{dt} + 30x = 0$$

$$\frac{d^2y}{dx^2} + 4\frac{dy}{dx} + 8y = 0$$

$$\frac{d^2y}{dx^2} + 5\frac{dy}{dx} + 6y = 3x + 2$$

$$\frac{d^2x}{dt^2} + 11\frac{dx}{dt} + 30x = 11 + 5t.$$

The test for linearity, is that the equation only contains the dependent variable and its derivatives and not products and functions of these.

If the terms involving the dependent variable and its derivatives are gathered together on the left hand side, and the other items set on the right hand side, then, if the right hand side is zero, the equation is called homogeneous.

If the right hand side is non-zero, then the equation is called non-homogeneous.

The first two examples above are homogeneous equations whilst the other two are non-homogeneous.

The general homogenous linear equation with constant coefficients has the form

$$a\frac{d^2x}{dt^2} + b\frac{dx}{dt} + cx = 0,$$

where a, b and c are constant.

The general non-homogeneous equation with constant coefficients has the form

$$a\frac{d^2x}{dt^2} + b\frac{dx}{dt} + cx = f(t),$$

where a, b and c are constant and f may depend on t but not x.

The corresponding forms with dependent variable y and independent variable x are obtained by replacing x by y and t by x.

The usual method of solving a non-homogeneous equation is a two-step one where the homogenous equation found by replacing the right hand side by zero is first solved. The method used for this is described in section 1.2. The solution of the non-homogeneous equation is then found by combining the solution of the homogeneous one with another function. This process is described in section 1.3. The following basic result is fundamental in understanding the method of solution described in section 1.2.

Basic result for linear homogeneous equations

The most important fact about a second order linear homogeneous equation is that it has two independent solutions (i.e. one not being directly proportional to the other) and that the general solution is found by multiplying each of the independent solutions by a different arbitrary constant and adding them together.

This means that if by any kind of guess work you can find two independent solutions you will know that there are no more and that the general solutions can be found from these. A simple example is

$$\frac{d^2x}{dt^2} - x = 0$$

you can check by substituting that e^t and e^{-t} are both solutions of the equation and therefore the general solution is $Ae^t + Be^{-t}$, where A and B are arbitrary constants.

For a first order homogeneous equation, which is obviously a particular case of a second order one, there is only one independent solution.

1.2　Solution of linear homogeneous equations

It is probably easier to understand the general method by first looking at a few examples.

Example 1.1

Find the general solution of

$$\frac{dx}{dt} - 4x = 0$$

The equation implies that $\frac{dx}{dt}$ is proportional to x. You also know that the derivative of e^{mt}, where m is a constant, is proportional to e^{mt}. This suggests that $x = ae^{mt}$, where a and m are constants, may be a solution provided m is chosen correctly. Substituting $x = ae^{mt}$ into the equation gives

$$mae^{mt} - 4ae^{mt} = 0,$$

the only way that this can be satisfied without A being zero is for m to be equal to 4. Therefore a solution is e^{4t}. You know from the basic result quoted above that there cannot be another independent solution and so the general solution is $x = ae^{4t}$.

Example 1.2

Find the general solution of
$$\frac{d^2 x}{dt^2} - 4x = 0$$

The first thing to do is to see whether or not the technique used in Example 1.1 will still work. Assuming that $x = ae^{mt}$ gives
$$m^2 ae^{mt} - 4ae^{mt} = 0$$

therefore, for a nontrivial solution $m^2 = 4$ and therefore $m = \pm 2$, so that two independent solutions are e^{2t} and e^{-2t}. The general solution is therefore
$$x = Ae^{2t} + Be^{-2t},$$

where A and B are arbitrary constants.

Example 1.3

Find the general solution of
$$\frac{d^2 y}{dx^2} + 3\frac{dy}{dx} + 2y = 0,$$

and the solution such that $y = 1$ and $\frac{dy}{dx} = 1$ for $x = 0$.

In this case, the independent variable is x and so the appropriate trial solution will be $y = ae^{mx}$. You should always remember to check that you are using the correct variables.

Substituting in the equation gives
$$m^2 ae^{mx} + 3mae^{mx} + 2ae^{mx} = 0$$
$$\left(m^2 + 3m + 2\right) ae^{mx}$$

and therefore, for a non-trivial solution (i.e. with $a \neq 0$)

$$m^2 + 3m + 2 = 0$$

The quadratic factorises as $(m+1)(m+2)$ and therefore the solutions are $m = -1$ and $m = -2$. The trial method has again produced the required two independent solutions, in this case e^{-x} and e^{-2x}. The general solution is therefore

$$y = Ae^{-x} + Be^{-2x}.$$

The next stage is to find the arbitrary constants so that the conditions at $x = 0$ are satisfied. The condition on y gives

$$A + B = 1,$$

also $$\frac{dy}{dx} = -Ae^{-x} - 2Be^{-2x},$$

and therefore the condition on $\dfrac{dy}{dx}$ at $x = 0$ gives

$$-A - 2B = 1$$

Solving these equations gives $B = -2$ and $A = 3$. The required solution is therefore

$$y = 3e^{-x} - 2e^{-2x}.$$

Example 1.4

Find the solution of
$$\frac{d^2x}{dt^2} + 2\frac{dx}{dt} + x = 0.$$

Making the substitution $x = ae^{mt}$ shows that m has to satisfy
$$m^2 + 2m + 1 = 0.$$

The roots of this quadratic are both –1 and therefore two independent solutions cannot be found. It is shown however in section 1.5 that if the root is repeated then if e^{mt} is a solution, then so is te^{mt}. It is worth verifying this in this problem. If $x = te^{-t}$, then

$$\frac{dx}{dt} = e^{-t} - te^{-t}, \qquad \frac{d^2x}{dt^2} = -2e^{-t} + te^{-t},$$

and substituting in the left hand side of the equation gives
$$-2e^{-t} + te^{-t} + 2\left(e^{-t} - te^{-t}\right) + te^{-t}.$$

This is zero, thus verifying that te^{-t} is also a solution. Therefore the general solution is

$$x = (At + B)e^{-t}$$

Example 1.5

Find the general solution of
$$\frac{d^2x}{dt^2} + x = 0$$

Making the trial substitution $x = ae^{mt}$ gives
$$m^2 ae^{mt} + ae^{mt} = 0$$

therefore $m^2 + 1 = 0$. The roots of this equation are not real but if you have met complex numbers, then you will know that the roots are $\pm i$ where $i = \sqrt{-1}$.

It is however not necessary to use complex numbers to make any progress but it is necessary to change tactics slightly. (A method using complex numbers is sketched in section 1.6).

In the given equation the second derivative of x is a positive multiple of $-x$. You know that both the sine and cosine have this behaviour and therefore possible trial substitutions might be $a \cos pt$ or $b \sin pt$ where p is a constant.

Making the substitutions gives

$$-p^2 a \cos pt + a \cos pt = 0 \quad \text{and} \quad -p^2 b \sin pt + b \sin pt = 0,$$

these equations will be satisfied if $p = \pm 1$. Therefore, taking $p = 1$ gives the two independent solutions $\cos t$ and $\sin t$. Taking $p = -1$ would give independent solutions $\cos(-t)$ and $\sin(-t)$, i.e. $\cos t$ and $-\sin t$, which are multiples of the same independent solutions as before. This was to be expected since there can only be two independent solutions. Therefore since two independent solutions have been found, the general solution is

$$x = A \cos t + B \sin t.$$

The trial method involving sines and cosines works for all equations of the form

$$\frac{d^2 x}{dt^2} + n^2 x = 0,$$

where n is real. In this case, independent solutions are $\cos nt$ and $\sin nt$ (you can check this by substituting in the equation) and the general solution is

$$x = A \cos nt + B \sin nt$$

Sometimes one of the alternative forms $x = a \cos(nt + \varepsilon)$ (a and ε are constants such that $A = a \cos \varepsilon$, $B = -a \sin \varepsilon$), (b and δ are constants such that $A = b \sin \delta$, $B = b \cos \delta$) are used, particularly in problems involving simple harmonic motion (see Chapter 3).

Example 1.6

Find the general solution of

$$\frac{d^2 x}{dt^2} + 2 \frac{dx}{dt} + 5x = 0$$

If $x = ae^{mt}$ is substituted with the above example, then, for $a \neq 0$, m must satisfy

$$m^2 + 2m + 5 = 0$$

This quadratic does not factorise and using the formula for the solution of a quadratic gives

$$m = \frac{-2 \pm \sqrt{4 - 20}}{2} = -1 \pm \sqrt{-4}$$

The roots are not real and if the notation is $i = \sqrt{-1}$ is used, the possible roots are $-1+2i$ and $-1 -2i$. It is possible, however, as in the previous example, to avoid complex numbers.

It is shown in section 1.6 that the independent solutions turn out to be $e^{-t}\cos 2t$ and $e^{-t}\sin 2t$ and we may now try to see how these arise.

Straight forward use of the roots suggests that independent solutions would be $e^{-t+t\sqrt{-4}}$ and $e^{-t-t\sqrt{-4}}$, but this is not particularly helpful unless you know what expressions like $e^{t\sqrt{-4}}$ means. The clue to what to do is the factor e^{-t} which suggests that x will be proportional to this. Therefore the substitution $x = ze^{-t}$ is made in the original equation.

Using the product rule shows that

$$\frac{dx}{dt} = \frac{dz}{dt}e^{-t} + ze^{-t}, \qquad \frac{d^2x}{dt^2} = \frac{d^2x}{dt^2}e^{-t} - 2\frac{dz}{dt}e^{-t} + ze^{-t},$$

and substituting into the differential equation gives

$$\frac{d^2z}{dt^2}e^{-t} - 2\frac{dz}{dt}e^{-t} + ze^{-t} + 2\left(\frac{dz}{dt}e^{-t} - ze^{-t}\right) + 5ze^{-t} = 0$$

This equation simplifies to

$$\frac{d^2z}{dt^2} + 4z = 0$$

and therefore it follows from the result quoted at the end of the previous example that independent solutions for z are $\cos 2t$ and $\sin 2t$. Therefore independent solution for x are $e^{-t}\cos 2t$ and $e^{-t}\sin 2t$ with the general solutions being

$$x = Ae^{-t}\cos 2t + Be^{-t}\sin 2t$$

The calculations was a bit long but the method works whenever the equation does not have real roots. It is shown in section 1.5 that the general solution when the roots are $p \pm \sqrt{-q}$, with $q > 0$, is $e^{pt}\left(A\cos\sqrt{q}t + B\sin\sqrt{q}t\right)$. You do not need to have to carry out the detail calculation but can usually quote this general result. You should, however, understand how the result was derived.

Example 1.7

Find the general solution of

$$\frac{d^2y}{dx^2} + 4\frac{dy}{dx} + 5y = 0,$$

and that solution such that $y = 0$ and $\frac{dy}{dx} = 1$ for $x = 0$.

Making the substitution $y = e^{mx}$ gives, as in other example

$$m^2 + 4m + 5 = 0$$

The solutions of this quadratic are

$$m = \frac{-4 \pm \sqrt{16 - 20}}{2} = -2 \pm \sqrt{-1}.$$

Therefore, using the above general result and remembering that the independent variable is now x, the general solution is
$$y = e^{-2x}\left(A\cos x + B\sin x\right).$$

The condition $y = 0$ for $x = 0$ shows that $A = 0$ and then
$$\frac{dy}{dx} = e^{-2x}\left(B\cos x - 2B\sin x\right).$$

Therefore $B = 1$ and the general solution is
$$y = e^{-2x}\sin x.$$

Summary of basic method

In summarising the method, x will be assumed to be the independent variable and t the dependent one and therefore the general equation considered will be
$$a\frac{d^2x}{dt^2} + b\frac{dx}{dt} + cx = 0,$$

where a, b and c are constants. You have however to be prepared for other variables.

(i) The first step is to make the trial substitutions $x = Ae^{mt}$, this means that for a non-zero solution m has to satisfy
$$am^2 + bm + c = 0.$$
This is called the auxiliary equation and is formed by replacing the second derivative by m^2, the first derivative by m and the dependent variable by 1.

(ii) (a) If there are two real roots m_1 and m_2, of the auxiliary equation, then the general solution is $x = Ae^{m_1t} + Be^{m_2t}$. (This case occurs in Examples 1.1., 1.2. and 1.3)

(b) If there is only one repeated root m, then the general solution is $x = e^{mt}\left(A + Bt\right)$. (This case occurs in Example 1.4).

(c) If the roots are not real but of the form $p \pm \sqrt{-q}$, where $q > 0$, the general solution is $x = e^{pt}\left(A\cos\sqrt{q}t + B\sin\sqrt{q}t\right)$. (This case occurs, with $p = 0$, in Example 1.5 and, for $p \neq 0$, in Examples 1.6 and 1.7).

(d) The special case when $p = 0$ corresponds to the differential equation
$$\frac{d^2x}{dt^2} + qx = 0,$$
whose general solution is therefore $x = A\cos\sqrt{q}t + B\sin\sqrt{q}t$.

Exercises 1.1

Find the general solutions of the following differential equations

1. $\dfrac{d^2x}{dt^2} - 9x = 0.$

2. $\dfrac{d^2x}{dt^2} - 3\dfrac{dx}{dt} + 2x = 0.$

3. $\dfrac{d^2x}{dt^2} - 8\dfrac{dx}{dt} + 17x = 0.$

4. $\dfrac{d^2y}{dx^2} - 6\dfrac{dy}{dx} + 8y = 0.$

5. $\dfrac{d^2y}{dx^2} + 8\dfrac{dy}{dx} + 80y = 0.$

6. $6\dfrac{d^2x}{dt^2} - 11\dfrac{dx}{dt} + 4x = 0.$

7. $\dfrac{d^2x}{dt^2} + 25x = 0.$

Find the solutions of the following differential equations under the conditions stated.

8. $\dfrac{d^2y}{dx^2} + 16y = 0,\ \ y = 3, \dfrac{dy}{dx} = 0$ for $x = \pi$.

9. $\dfrac{d^2x}{dt^2} - 4\dfrac{dx}{dt} + 20x = 0,\ x = 2, \dfrac{dx}{dt} = 4$ for $t = 0$.

10. $\dfrac{d^2x}{dt^2} + 7\dfrac{dx}{dt} + 10x = 0,\ x = 5, \dfrac{dx}{dt} = 11$ for $t = 0$.

11. $\dfrac{d^2y}{dx^2} + 8\dfrac{dy}{dx} + 41y = 0,\ y = 0, \dfrac{dy}{dx} = 1$ for $x = \pi$.

12. $\dfrac{d^2x}{dt^2} - \dfrac{dx}{dt} - 6x = 0,\ x = 5, \dfrac{dx}{dt} = 5$ for $t = 0$.

13. $\dfrac{d^2y}{dx^2} + 8\dfrac{dy}{dx} + 20y = 0,\ y = 2, \dfrac{dy}{dx} = 4$ for $x = 0$.

1.3 Solution of inhomogeneous equations

The method of solution depends on the following fundamental result :

The general solution of a linear inhomogeneous differential equation (i.e. one with a non-zero right hand side) is the sum of the solution of the corresponding homogeneous equation (i.e. with zero right hand side) and any solution of the inhomogeneous equation.

The solution of the homogeneous equation is called the Complementary Function (C.F.) and any solution of the inhomogeneous equation is called the Particular Integral (P.I.). Therefore

General solution = Complementary Function + Particular Integral.

It does not matter how the Particular Integral is found as long as you check that it is a solution. In your course, if the independent variable is t, then the only right hand sides that you will come across will be of the form $At + B$, where A and B are constants i.e. the equations will be of the form

$$a\frac{d^2x}{dt^2} + b\frac{dx}{dt} + cx = At + B.$$

The method of finding the Particular Integral is very simple, you assume that, if $A \neq 0$, $x = Ct + D$, and if $A = 0$, $x = D$. The appropriate form is substituted in the equation and the constants C and D chosen so that the equation is satisfied. In some particular cases (in fact when one of the roots of the auxiliary equation is zero) you may find this substitution does not work. In that case try $x = Ct^2 + Dt$.

Summary

(a) Find the general solution of the corresponding homogeneous equation - the C.F.

(b) By making the trial substitution $x = Ct + D$ (or, exceptionally, if it does not work, $x = Ct^2 + Dt$) find the P.I.

(c) Write the general solution as C.F. + P.I.

Example 1.8

Find a particular integral for the differential equation

$$\frac{d^2x}{dt^2} + 8\frac{dx}{dt} + 4x = 56 + 20t.$$

Making the trial substitution $x = Ct + D$ in the left hand side of the equation gives

$$8C + 4(Ct + D) = 56 + 20t.$$

The coefficients of t have to be the same on both sides of the equation, and also the constant terms, and therefore $C = 5$, and $8C + 4D = 56$ so that $D = 4$. A particular integral is therefore $5t + 4$.

Example 1.9

Find the general solution of

$$2\frac{d^2x}{dt^2} + 3\frac{dx}{dt} = 24 + 18t.$$

The first step is to solve the equation with zero right hand side, the auxiliary equation is

$$2m^2 + 3m = 0.$$

The solutions are $m = 0$ and $m = -\dfrac{3}{2}$ so the C.F. is $A + Be^{-\frac{3}{2}t}$.

Making the trial substitution $x = Ct + D$ into the left hand side of the differential equation gives
$$3C = 24 + 18t.$$

Since C is a constant this equation cannot be satisfied and therefore the trial substitution $x = Ct^2 + Dt$ is made into the right hand side of the differential equation giving
$$4C + 3(2Ct + D) = 24 + 18t.$$

The coefficients of t and the constant terms have to be the same on both sides of the equation so that $6C = 18$ and $4C + 3D = 24$ and therefore $C = 3$ and $D = 4$.

The general solution is therefore
$$x = A + Be^{-\frac{3}{2}t} + 3t^2 + 4t.$$

This example is the exceptional case mentioned earlier.

Example 1.10

Find the general solution of
$$\frac{d^2 y}{dx^2} + 3\frac{dy}{dx} + 2y = 16 + 4x,$$

and that solution such that $y = 12$ and $\dfrac{dy}{dx} = -5$ for $x = 0$.

The first step is to find the general solution of the equation with zero right hand side. This has already been done in Example 3.11 and the general solution is $Ae^{-x} + Be^{-2x}$. Making the trial substitution $y = Cx + D$ in the left hand side of the equation gives
$$3C + 2(Cx + D) = 16 + 4x.$$

The coefficients of x have to be the same on both sides of the equation and therefore $C = 2$, and $3C + 2D = 16$ so that $D = 5$. The general solution of the equation is therefore
$$y = Ae^{-x} + Be^{-2x} + 2x + 5.$$

The final step is to find the constants so that the conditions for $x = 0$ are satisfied. These require
$$A + B + 5 = 12 \quad \text{and} \quad -A - 2B + 2 = -5,$$
the solution of these equations is $A = 7$, $B = 0$.

The complete solution is
$$y = 7e^{-x} + 2x + 5.$$

Exercises 1.2

Find the general solutions of the following differential equations.

1     $\dfrac{d^2x}{dt^2} - 5\dfrac{dx}{dt} + 6x = 12.$

2     $\dfrac{d^2x}{dt^2} - 6\dfrac{dx}{dt} + 5x = 3 + 10t.$

3     $\dfrac{d^2x}{dt^2} + 10\dfrac{dx}{dt} + 26x = 52.$

4     $\dfrac{d^2x}{dt^2} + 2\dfrac{dx}{dt} + 10x = 30t - 34.$

5     $\dfrac{d^2y}{dx^2} + 11\dfrac{dy}{dx} + 24y = 57 + 72x.$

6     $\dfrac{d^2y}{dx^2} + 4\dfrac{dy}{dx} = 3 + 8x.$

Find the solutions of the following differential equations under the stated conditions

7     $\dfrac{d^2x}{dt^2} + 8\dfrac{dx}{dt} - 20x = -60$, $x = 8, \dfrac{dx}{dt} = 4$ for $t = 0.$

8     $\dfrac{d^2x}{dt^2} + 4\dfrac{dx}{dt} + 20x = 80, x = 7, \dfrac{dx}{dt} = -6$ for $t = 0.$

9     $\dfrac{d^2y}{dx^2} + 2\dfrac{dy}{dx} + y = 10 + 3x, y = 4, \dfrac{dy}{dx} = 4$ for $x = 0.$

10     $\dfrac{d^2y}{dx^2} + 4\dfrac{dy}{dx} + 20y = 80, y = 7, \dfrac{dy}{dx} = -6$ for $x = 0.$

1.4   Problems involving second order equations

In some instances, primarily in Economics, the actual model involves more than one equation. If, for example, x denotes the price of a good and D and S denote the demand (quantity required at price x) and supply (amount supplied at price x), then in one economic model, the rate of change of price is asserted to be directly proportional to the excess of demand over supply (price increases when demand exceeds supply). This gives

$$\frac{dx}{dt} = k(D - S),$$

where $k > 0$. In order to complete the modelling, some information has to be given about D and S. The usual assumption is that both are of the $a + bx$ and this gives a first order differential equation for x. In slightly more complicated models D and S are assumed to depend on the time derivatives of x and this leads to second order differential equations. Very often a model may be posed in a way that leads to two first order equations involving more than one variable and one of the variables has to be eliminated thus giving a second order equation.

Example 1.11

This is a simple model of investment due to Samuelson. The assumptions are

(i) the rate of change of capital at any time is equal to the investment at that time,

(ii) the rate of change of investment at any time is s times the difference between the capital at that time and an equilibrium value A. Investment increases when the capital level is less than A and decreases when the level is above A.

Find the differential equation satisfied by the investment and comment on the behaviour of the capital.

There are two "unknowns" i.e. dependent variables, namely the investment and the capital. These will be donated by I and C respectively. Assumption (i) gives

$$\frac{dC}{dt} = I$$

whilst assumption (ii) gives

$$\frac{dI}{dt} = -s(C - A)$$

The second equation satisfies the condition that I decreases (increases) for $C > A$ $(C < A)$.

Differentiating the second equation with respect to t gives

$$\frac{d^2 I}{dt^2} = -s \frac{dC}{dt}$$

and substituting from the first equation gives

$$\frac{d^2 I}{dt^2} = -sI \ .$$

The auxiliary equation for this differential equation is $m^2 = -s$ with roots $\sqrt{-s}$ and therefore, from the summary in section 3.5, its general solution is $B \cos \sqrt{s}t + C \sin \sqrt{s}t$.

The capital is therefore

$$A - \frac{1}{s} \frac{dI}{dt} = A - \frac{1}{\sqrt{s}} \left(-B \sin \sqrt{s}t + C \cos \sqrt{s}t \right).$$

Both the sine and cosine terms have period $\dfrac{2\pi}{\sqrt{s}}$ and therefore the capital oscillates

with this period.

Example 1.12

The amount of steel ingots that a firm has in stock at any time is denoted by x and the firm has an optimum amount X of ingot that it wishes to retain in stock.

Its pricing policy is that the rate of increase of price is equal to the difference between x and X with the price increasing for $x < X$ and decreasing for $x > X$. The rate of increase of stock is the difference between the rate Q at which ingots are produced and the rate S at which they are sold. The firm assumes in its forecasting that, in appropriate units, Q and S are given in terms of the price p by

$$S = 120 - 35p - 10\frac{dp}{dt} \text{ and } Q = 48 - 11p.$$

Find the differential equations satisfied by p and show that the model predicts p will tend to be a fixed value and find this value.

The pricing policy gives

$$\frac{dp}{dt} = (X - x)$$

Also, the condition governing the rate of increase of stock gives

$$\frac{dx}{dt} = Q - S = -72 + 24p + 10\frac{dp}{dt}.$$

Differentiating the first differential equation gives

$$\frac{d^2p}{dt^2} = -\frac{dx}{dt}$$

and therefore substituting for $\frac{dx}{dt}$ gives

$$\frac{d^2p}{dt^2} + 10\frac{dp}{dt} + 24p = 72$$

The auxiliary equation is

$$m^2 + 10m + 24 = 0,$$

Its roots are –6 and –4 and therefore the general solution is $ae^{-4t} + be^{-6t}$.

Since the right hand side is constant, the particular integral will be a constant and therefore substituting $p = C$, where C is a constant, in the equation gives $C = 3$ and therefore

$$p = 3 + ae^{-4t} + be^{-6t}.$$

The exponentials tend to zero for large t and therefore the price tends to 3.

Modelling problems in Mechanics using differential equations

Detail modelling of various problems in Mechanics will be considered in Chapters 2 and 3, but it is worth examining briefly the basic principles involved. Unlike the other problems considered, the basic laws governing mechanical problems are well known. Essentially for a particle in rectilinear motion, the important points are to find the total force acting and put this equal to mass × acceleration.

It is extremely important in modelling problems to choose a particular reference direction, usually the positive x direction, and calculate the force in that direction. The acceleration is $\dfrac{d^2x}{dt^2}$ and therefore multiplying this by the mass and putting it equal to the force in the positive x direction will produce the required differential equation. It is however necessary to be extremely careful with signs, this is shown in the following example.

Example 1.13

A particle of mass 0.2kg is free to move along the x-axis under the action of a force directed towards the origin and of magnitude $4d$ N, where d m is the distance of the particle from the origin. The particle is also subject to a resistive force (i.e. in the opposite direction to its motion) of magnitude $2v$ N when it is moving with speed $v\,\mathrm{ms}^{-1}$. Find its equation of motion.

If the particle is on the positive x-axis, then its distance from the origin is x m, the attractive force is to the left as shown in the diagram and of magnitude $4x$ N, the force in the positive x direction is therefore $-4x$ N. If the particle is on the negative x-axis, then its distance from the origin is $(-x)$ m, $(-x$ is positive), the attractive force is to the right as shown in the diagram and of magnitude $4(-x)$ N, the force in the positive x direction is therefore again $-4x$ N.

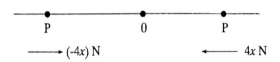

If the particle is moving to the right then $\dfrac{dx}{dt}$ is positive and is the speed of the particle, the resistive force is therefore to the left and equal to $12\dfrac{dx}{dt}$ N, the force in the positive x direction is therefore $-12\dfrac{dx}{dt}$ N.

If the particle is moving to the left then $\dfrac{dx}{dt}$ is negative and the speed of the particle is $-\dfrac{dx}{dt}$, (which is positive) and the resistive force is to the right and equal to $12\left(-\dfrac{dx}{dt}\right)$ N. The force in the positive x direction is therefore $-12\left(\dfrac{dx}{dt}\right)$ N.

Therefore the equation of motion is

$$0.2\frac{d^2x}{dt^2} = -4x - 12\frac{dx}{dt}.$$

This type of equation can be solved as in section 1.2 and the resulting motion is referred to as damped harmonic motion. This is looked at in detail in Chapter 3.

It is very important when formulating a new model, to look very carefully at the signs as above. If the force had been proportional to d^2, for example, then the differential equations found would have been different for $x > 0$ and $x < 0$.

1.5　Justification of the methods for equal and for non-real roots

The general type of equation considered is

$$a\frac{d^2x}{dt^2} + b\frac{dx}{dt} + cx = 0,$$

where a, b and c are constants.

The auxiliary equation is

$$am^2 + bm + c = 0$$

with solutions

$$\frac{-b \pm \sqrt{b^2 - 4ac}}{2a} = \frac{-b}{2a} \pm \frac{\sqrt{b^2 - 4ac}}{2a}$$

Equal Roots

For equal roots $b^2 = 4ac$ and the only distinct root of the auxiliary equation is $-\dfrac{b}{2a}$

and this is denoted by p. It is now necessary to show that $x = te^{pt}$ is also a solution. The product rule shows that

$$\frac{dx}{dt} = e^{pt}(1 + pt), \qquad \frac{d^2x}{dt^2} = e^{pt}(2p + p^2t).$$

Substituting these in the left hand side of the differential equation gives

$$a(2p + p^2t) + b(1 + pt) + ct = b + 2ap + (c + p^2a + pb)t,$$

since $p = -\dfrac{b}{2a}$, the right hand side of the equation simplifies to $\left(c - \dfrac{b^2}{4a}\right)t$.

This vanishes and hence $te^{pt}\left(= te^{-\frac{bt}{2a}}\right)$ is also a solution of the differential equation.

Non-real (i.e. complex) roots

In this case when $b^2 - 4ac < 0$ and the roots are $p \pm \sqrt{-q}$, where $p = -\dfrac{b}{2a}$ and

$q = \dfrac{4ac - b^2}{4a^2}$ and is positive. The first step in deriving the form given in the summary in section 1.2 , as in Example 1.6, is to write x as ze^{pt}. If you want to try this for any particular equation, then the coefficient of t in the exponential is minus one half the ratio of the coefficient of the first derivative to that of the second derivative.

Using the product rule

$$\frac{dx}{dt} = e^{pt}\left(\frac{dz}{dt} + pz\right)$$

$$\frac{d^2x}{dt^2} = e^{pt}\left(\frac{d^2z}{dt^2} + 2p\frac{dz}{dt} + p^2z\right).$$

Substituting these in the equation gives

$$a\left(\frac{d^2z}{dt^2} + 2p\frac{dz}{dt} + p^2z\right) + b\left(\frac{dz}{dt} + pz\right) + cz = 0.$$

Substituting $p = -\dfrac{b}{2a}$ shows that the coefficient of $\dfrac{dz}{dt}$ is zero and the equation becomes

$$a\frac{d^2z}{dt^2} + \left(c + p^2a + pb\right)z = 0.$$

This simplifies on substituting for p and using the definition $q = \dfrac{4ac - b^2}{4a^2}$ to

$$\frac{d^2z}{dt^2} + qz = 0.$$

Making the trial substitution $z = A\cos mt + B\sin mt$ shows that

$$-m^2 + q = 0,$$

and therefore $m = \sqrt{q}$, giving the general solution $z = A\cos\sqrt{q}t + B\sin\sqrt{q}t$.
Therefore the general solution for x is $e^{pt}\left(A\cos\sqrt{q}t + B\sin\sqrt{q}t\right)$, thus confirming he assertion made in the summary in Section 1.2.

For those familiar with complex numbers the following is an alternative derivation.
The roots of the auxiliary equation can be written as $p \pm i\sqrt{q}$. The general solution is therefore $Ce^{pt}e^{i\sqrt{q}t} + De^{pt}e^{-i\sqrt{q}t}$. This can be rewritten, using the result

$$e^{\pm i\theta} = \cos\theta \pm i\sin\theta$$

as

$$e^{pt}\left[C\left(\cos\sqrt{q}t + i\sin\sqrt{q}t\right) + D\left(\cos\sqrt{q}t - i\sin\sqrt{q}t\right)\right]$$

This can be rewritten as

$$e^{pt}\left(A\cos\sqrt{q}t + B\sin\sqrt{q}t\right),$$

where $A = C + D$ and $B = i(C - D)$.

Miscellaneous Exercises 1

1. Find the general solution of
    $$\frac{d^2y}{dx^2} + 2\frac{dy}{dx} + 10y = 30x + 16$$

2. Find the general solution of
    $$\frac{d^2y}{dx^2} + 7\frac{dy}{dx} + 12y = 36$$

3. (a) Find the general solution of
    $$\frac{d^2x}{dx^2} + 15\frac{dx}{dt} + 36x = k \qquad \text{where } k \text{ is a constant.}$$

    Find also that solution such that $x = 0$ and $\dfrac{dx}{dt} = 0$ at $t = 0$.

   (b) Initially a community consists of N individuals all of whom are susceptible to a disease. Subsequently each member of the community may be placed in one, and only one, of the following categories.
   *   Individuals who are susceptible to the disease,
   *   individuals currently infected by the disease,
   *   individuals recovered from the disease and not open to further infection,
   *   individuals who have died from the disease.

   At time t after the infection strikes, x denotes the number that have died and y the number currently infected. The death rate and the recovery rate are such that, at any instant, the number that have recovered is twice the number who have died by that time. Write down, in terms of x and y and N, the number of susceptible people at time t. Given that, at any instant, the rate at which susceptible people become infected is (in appropriate units) three times the number of susceptible people present at that instant, show that
   $$3\frac{dx}{dt} + \frac{dy}{dt} = 3(N - 3x - y)$$

   Given that the death rate of infected people is four times the number of infected people, express $\dfrac{dx}{dt}$ in terms of y and hence show that x satisfies the equation in

   (a) for a particular value of k, which should be found. Assuming no one dies from other causes, state how many people will eventually die from the disease.

4. (a) Find the general solution of the differential equation
    $$\frac{d^2x}{dt^2} + 4\frac{dx}{dt} + 8x = 0.$$

   (b) In economic modelling of investment it is assumed, with a particular choice of units, that
    (i) the rate of increase of excess capital k is equal to the investment I,

(ii) the rate of decrease of the investment I is equal to the sum of $8k$ and $4I$.

Express $\dfrac{dk}{dt}$ in terms of I, and $\dfrac{dI}{dt}$ in terms of k and I, and hence show that k satisfies the differential equation in part (a). Comment on the behaviour of k for large values of t.

5. Find the solution of
$$\frac{d^2 p}{dt^2} + 2\frac{dp}{dt} + 17p = 34,$$

such that $p = 2.5$ and $\dfrac{dp}{dt} = 0$ when $t = 0$.

In an economic model, the demand D (the amount required) for a particular item is given by
$$D = 6\frac{d^2 p}{dt^2} + 7\frac{dp}{dt} + 6p + 16,$$

where p is the price in pounds of the item at time t months. Similarly the supply S (the amount available) is given by
$$S = 7\frac{d^2 p}{dt^2} + 9\frac{dp}{dt} = 23p - 18.$$

Given that $S = D$ and that, at $t = 0$, $p = 2.5$ and $\dfrac{dp}{dt} = 0$, find

(i) the price after a long time,

(ii) the lowest price at which the item can be bought and the time when this would be possible.

6. The function y satisfies the differential equation
$$\frac{d^2 y}{dx^2} - 4\frac{dy}{dx} + (4 - k)y = k(k + 1)(6x + 4)$$

where k is a constant, and, when $x = 0$, $y = 5$ and $\dfrac{dy}{dx} = -1$.

Find y in the three cases

(a) $k = 1$,

(b) $k = -1$,

(c) $k = 0$.

7. Find the solution of
$$\frac{d^2 x}{dt^2} = 16x$$

with $x = a$ and $\dfrac{dx}{dt} = -b$ at $t = 0$, where a and b are positive constants.

Verify that if $a > \dfrac{b}{4}$, then x will never become zero and $\dfrac{dx}{dt}$ will be zero for a positive value of t.

It is assumed in a simple "war game" that there are two military force, the 'A-force' and the 'B-force', engaged in combat. The numbers in the A-force and the B-force at time t are denoted by x and y respectively. It is also assumed that the rate at which the number in the A-force is decreasing is equal to twice the number in the B-force at that time and that the number in the B-force is decreasing at a rate equal to eight times the number in the A-force at that time. Show that x satisfies the above differential equation.

The game is won when one of the forces is annihilated and the other is not. Given that x_0 and y_0 denote the numbers in the A-force and the B-force respectively at time $t = 0$, find a condition on x_0 and y_0 which will ensure that the A-force wins the game.

Chapter 2

Rectilinear Motion

After working through this chapter you should

- be able to solve problems of rectilinear motion where the acceleration is a function of displacement or velocity,
- be able to solve simple problems of resisted rectilinear motion,
- be aware of some of the assumptions made in modelling resistive forces.

2.1   Acceleration dependent on displacement

You have already seen in M1 Chapter 4, how to solve problems of motion in a straight line where the acceleration depended on time. In this chapter problems where the acceleration depends on displacement or on velocity will be considered. The basic difference between these problems and those you met in M1 is that the problems now involve differential equations which need the methods described in Chapter 1 to solve them. In M1 the acceleration a was defined by

$$a = \frac{dv}{dt} = \frac{d^2x}{dt^2} \; ,$$

where v is the velocity in the positive x direction and is defined by

$$v = \frac{dx}{dt} .$$

There is another expression for a which is useful for problems where the acceleration is given in terms of the displacement and this is

$$a = v\frac{dv}{dx} .$$

This is proved by using the identity

$$\frac{dv}{dt} = \frac{dv}{dx}\frac{dx}{dt} ,$$

which follows from the chain rule.

Substituting v for $\frac{dx}{dt}$ gives the required expression for a.

The general approach is possibly most easily understood by looking at a particular example.

Example 2.1

When the displacement of a particle from a point O is x m its acceleration is e^{2x} ms^{-2}. At time $t = 0$, the particle passes through the origin moving with speed 1 ms^{-1} in the direction of increasing x. Find

(a) its speed when its displacement is x m,

(b) its displacement at time t s.

The equation of motion of the particle is

$$\frac{d^2x}{dt^2} = e^{2x},$$

this equation cannot be integrated directly with respect to t since the right-hand side involves x which is not known in terms of t. However, the equation of motion can, using the expression derived above, be rewritten as

$$v\frac{dv}{dt} = e^{2x}.$$

The left-hand side is equal to $d\left(\dfrac{\frac{1}{2}v^2}{dx}\right)$

i.e.

$$d\left(\frac{\frac{1}{2}v^2}{dx}\right) = e^{2x}.$$

Both sides of this equation can be integrated with respect to x giving

$$\frac{1}{2}v^2 = \frac{1}{2}e^{2x} + c,$$

where c is a constant. Substituting $v = 1$ when $x = 0$ shows that $c = 0$. Therefore, on taking the square root,

$$v = e^x.$$

It is necessary to be very careful in choosing the correct sign for the square root in problems like this, in this case the positive sign has to be chosen since the particle was moving in the positive x direction when $x = 0$ and therefore

$$\frac{dx}{dt} = e^x.$$

This is a differential equation to determine x and it can be solved by separation of variables. Separating the variables gives

$$e^{-x}\frac{dx}{dt} = 1,$$

which on integrating with respect to t becomes

$$\int e^{-x}\, dx = \int dt.$$

Carrying out the integrations gives

$$-e^{-x} = t + a,$$

where a is a constant. Substituting $x = 0$ and $t = 0$ shows that $a = -1$, therefore

$$x = -\ln(1 - t).$$

The solution is only valid for $t < 1$ as x becomes infinite for $t = 1$. The example is not a physically realistic one but the mathematics is sufficiently simple for the steps to be clear.

Basic method

When the acceleration is given in terms of the displacement the following are the steps to be followed:-

(i) Write the acceleration as

$$v\frac{dv}{dx} = \frac{d\left(\frac{1}{2}v^2\right)}{dx}.$$

(ii) Integrate the resulting equation with respect to x.

(ii) Use any given conditions to find the arbitrary constant produced by the integration in (i) Alternatively it may be quicker to integrate between suitable limits.

(iii) You will now have an expression for v^2. Take the appropriate square root so that your value for v is consistent with the given conditions.

(iv) The result of (iii) will be of the form

$$v = \frac{dx}{dt} = F(x),$$

where F is known in terms of x.

(v) The equation found in (iv) can be solved by separating the variables and integrating with respect to t giving

$$\int \frac{dx}{F(x)} = \int dt$$

Carrying out the integrations gives t in terms of x. If possible the resulting equation should be inverted to give x in terms of t.

In many cases the integration in (v) may prove very difficult and it may be necessary to use a numerical method like Simpson's rule to go any further.

Therefore very often, when the acceleration is given in terms of the displacement, the most that can be found easily is a relation between the velocity and the displacement. The basic method is equivalent to using the work-energy principle as described in M2.

If the velocity, rather than the acceleration, is given in terms of the displacement then the calculation will start at (v).

Example 2.2

The acceleration due to gravity at a point away from the earth is directed towards O, the centre of the earth, and is equal to $\dfrac{ga^2}{x^2}$, where a denotes the radius of the earth and x the distance from O. The fuel in a rocket is completely exhausted when it is at a distance b from the earth's centre and the speed of the rocket at that time is u. Assuming that the rocket moves along the straight line to it from O, find its speed when it is at a distance of $\dfrac{5b}{4}$ from O.

The acceleration in the direction of increasing x is $-\dfrac{ga^2}{x^2}$ and therefore the equation of motion can be written as

$$v\frac{dv}{dx} = \frac{d\left(\frac{1}{2}v^2\right)}{dx} = -\frac{ga^2}{x^2}.$$

If the required velocity is denoted by V then integrating the left-hand side with respect to v from u to V and the right-hand side with respect to x from b to $\dfrac{5b}{4}$ gives

$$V^2 - u^2 = -\frac{2ga^2}{5b},$$

and therefore the required speed is $\sqrt{\left(u^2 - \dfrac{2ga^2}{5b}\right)}$.

This will only be valid for $u^2 > \dfrac{2ga^2}{5b}$.

If $u^2 < \dfrac{2ga^2}{5b}$ then the rocket will have come to rest before reaching the point at a distance of $\dfrac{5b}{4}$ from O and will then return to earth.

Example 2.3

When the displacement of a particle from a point O is x m its acceleration is $\dfrac{24}{x^4}$ ms^{-2} in the direction of decreasing x. At time $t = 0$, the particle passes through the point $x = 2$ moving with speed $\sqrt{2}$ ms^{-1} in the direction of increasing x. Find

(a) its speed when its displacement is x m,

(b) its displacement at time t s.

The equation of motion of the particle is

$$v \frac{dv}{dx} = \frac{d\left(\frac{1}{2} v^2\right)}{dx} = -\frac{24}{x^4}.$$

Integrating this equation with respect to x gives

$$\frac{1}{2} v^2 = \frac{8}{x^3} + c,$$

where c is a constant. Substituting $v = \sqrt{2}$ when $x = 2$ shows that $c = 0$. Therefore, on taking the square root,

$$v = \frac{4}{x^{\frac{3}{2}}}.$$

The positive sign has been chosen since the particle was moving in the positive x direction when $x = 2$. Therefore

$$\frac{dx}{dt} = \frac{4}{x^{\frac{3}{2}}}$$

Separating the variables gives

$$x^{\frac{3}{2}} \frac{dx}{dt} = 4,$$

which becomes, on integrating with respect to t,

$$\int x^{\frac{3}{2}} \, dx = 4 \int d t.$$

Carrying out the integrations gives

$$\frac{2}{5} x^{\frac{5}{2}} = 4t + a,$$

where a is a constant. Substituting $x = 2$ for $t = 0$ shows that $a = \frac{8\sqrt{2}}{5}$ and inverting the equation gives

$$x = \left(4\sqrt{2} + 10t\right)^{\frac{2}{5}}$$

Example 2.4

The acceleration in the positive x direction of a particle free to move along the x axis is $-\omega^2 x$, where ω is a constant. At time $t = 0$ the particle is at rest at the point $x = a$. Determine its subsequent displacement. (This is an example of simple harmonic motion which you will encounter in detail in Chapter 3).

In this case the equation of motion of the particle is

$$v\frac{dv}{dx} = \frac{d\frac{1}{2}v^2}{dx} = -\omega^2 x.$$

Integrating this equation with respect to x gives

$$v^2 = -\omega^2 x^2 + c,$$

where c is a constant. Substituting $v = 0$ when $x = a$ shows that $c = \omega^2 a^2$. Therefore, on taking the square root,

$$v = -\omega\sqrt{a^2 - x^2},$$

the negative sign has been chosen since the particle was at rest at $x = a$ and its acceleration is in the negative x direction and therefore the particle will start moving in the negative x direction. Therefore

$$\frac{dx}{dt} = -\omega\sqrt{a^2 - x^2}.$$

Separating the variables and integrating gives

$$\int\frac{dx}{\omega\sqrt{a^2 - x^2}} = -\omega\int dt.$$

The integral with respect to x can be evaluated so that

$$\sin^{-1}\left(\frac{x}{a}\right) = -\omega t + b,$$

where b is a constant. Substituting $x = a$ when $t = 0$ shows that $b = \frac{\pi}{2}$ and finally

$$x = a\cos\omega t.$$

Exercises 2.1

1 The acceleration of a particle moving along the x axis is $4x$ ms^{-1} in the negative x direction when its displacement from the origin is x m. The particle is released from rest at the point $x = 3$. Find its speed when $x = 2$.

2 A particle moves along the x axis and its acceleration is $8x^3$ ms^{-2}, in the direction of increasing x, when its displacement from the origin is x m. It is moving in the direction of increasing x with speed 3 ms^{-1} when it passes through the origin. Find the distance travelled until its speed becomes 6 ms^{-1}.

3 When a particle has a displacement of x m from the origin its acceleration in the negative x direction is $\dfrac{3}{2x^2}$ ms^{-2}. Its velocity when $x = 0.25$ m is 3 ms^{-1} in the positive x direction. Find the speed in terms of the displacement and determine where the particle first comes to instantaneous rest.

In questions 4 to 8 the acceleration of a particle moving along the x axis is denoted by $f(x)$ ms^{-2} when its displacement from the origin at time t s is x m and v denotes the velocity component in the positive x direction.

4   $f = -\dfrac{16}{x^3}$, $v = 2$, for $x = 2$ when $t = 0$.   Find v in terms of x and x in terms of t.

5   $f = (x + 5)$, $v = 5$, for $x = 0$ when $t = 0$.   Find v in terms of x and x in terms of t.

6   $f = e^{2x}$, $v = 2$, for $x = \ln 2$ when $t = 0$.   Find v in terms of x and x in terms of t.

7   $f = 3\sqrt{x}$, $v = 0$, for $x = 0$ when $t = 0$.   Find v in terms of x and x in terms of t.

8   $f = \dfrac{1}{x^3}$, $v = 0$, for $x = 1$ when $t = 0$.   Find the time taken to reach the point $x = \dfrac{1}{2}$.

9   The acceleration due to gravity at a point at a distance of x m above the earth's centre is directed towards the centre of the earth and is of magnitude $10\left(\dfrac{6.4 \times 10^6}{x}\right)^2$ ms^{-2}. The earth may be assumed to be a sphere of radius 6.4×10^6 m. Find the maximum height reached above the earth's surface by a rocket projected vertically upwards from the earth's surface with speed 1000 ms^{-1}. The rocket is to be modelled as a particle projected vertically upwards in vacuum.

2.2   Acceleration dependent on velocity

Most problems involving resisted motion reduce to ones where the acceleration is given in terms of the velocity. The resulting differential equations have to be solved, usually by using the method of separation of variables.

There is a standard general approach which has to be followed and, as in the previous section, this is possibly best understood by working through a particular example.

Example 2.5

The acceleration of a particle moving with speed v ms^{-1} at time t s is $\dfrac{1}{v^2}$ ms^{-2}. When $t = 0$, $v = 1$ and the particle is at a distance of 4 m from a point O. Find the speed and displacement of the particle from O at any subsequent time and also its speed when at a distance of 6 m from O.

The equation of motion is

$$\frac{d^2x}{dt^2} = \frac{dv}{dt} = \frac{1}{v^2},$$

in this case using acceleration as $\dfrac{d^2x}{dt^2}$ does not help but the alternative form as $\dfrac{dv}{dt}$ gives a differential equation which can be integrated by separation of variables.

Therefore

$$\int v^2 \, dv = \int dt.$$

Carrying out the integrations gives

$$\frac{v^3}{3} = t + c,$$

where c is a constant. Substituting $v = 1$ when $t = 0$ shows that $c = \dfrac{1}{3}$.

Therefore

$$v = (1 + 3t)^{\frac{1}{3}}.$$

The next step is to find the displacement, x m. Substituting $\dfrac{dx}{dt}$ for v gives

$$\frac{dx}{dt} = (1 + 3t)^{\frac{1}{3}}.$$

This can be integrated directly with respect to t, you can do this either by introducing a constant or integrating between limits. The second method is slightly quicker and integrating from $t = 0$ to $t = t$ gives, since $x = 4$ when $t = 0$,

$$x - 4 = \int_0^t (1 + 3w)^{\frac{1}{3}} \, dw = \frac{(1 + 3t)^{\frac{4}{3}} - 1}{4},$$

and therefore

$$x = \frac{(1 + 3t)^{\frac{4}{3}} + 15}{4}.$$

The next step is to find the speed when $x = 6$. Substituting $x = 6$ in the expression for x gives $(1 + 3t)^{\frac{4}{3}} = 9$ and therefore $(1 + 3t)^{\frac{1}{3}} = \sqrt{3}$ so that substituting for t in the expression for $\dfrac{dx}{dt}$ gives the required speed as $\sqrt{3}$ ms^{-1}.

If the speed had been required for a general value of x then inverting the expression for x gives

$$(1 + 3t) = (4x - 15)^{\frac{3}{4}}$$

and therefore

$$\frac{dx}{dt} = (4x - 15)^{\frac{1}{4}}.$$

If the question had only required the relationship between v and x then a quicker method would have been to use the expression $v\dfrac{dv}{dx}$ for the acceleration. In this case the equation of motion would be

$$v\frac{dv}{dx} = \frac{1}{v^2}.$$

The method of separation of variables gives

$$\int v^3 dv = \int dx,$$

integrating the left hand side from $v = 1$ to $v = v$ and the right hand side from $x = 4$ to $x = x$ gives

$$v^4 - 1 = 4x - 16,$$

which is the result found earlier.

Whenever the acceleration is given as a function of speed the steps in the calculation will be exactly the same as in Example 2.5.

General approach

(i) Use the acceleration in the form $\dfrac{dv}{dt}$ in the equation of motion, separate the variables and integrate, either introducing a constant of integration or integrating between limits. If an arbitrary constant is introduced then use given conditions to find it. If the acceleration is directly proportional to v then an alternative is to use the substitution $v = e^{mt}$.

(ii) This will give v in terms of t, this can be integrated using $v = \dfrac{dx}{dt}$ to find x in terms of t. Again either integrate between limits or introduce an arbitrary constant. If an arbitrary constant is introduced then use given conditions to find it.

(iii) If a relation between v and x is required then

either

(a) Invert the solution found in step (ii) to give t in terms of x and substitute the result in the expression for v found in step (i). If it is not possible to carry out this inversion it may be possible to invert the expression for v to find t in terms of v and therefore x can be found in terms of v.

or

(b) Use the acceleration in the form $v\dfrac{dv}{dx}$ in the equation of motion, separate the variables and integrate, either introducing a constant of integration or integrating between limits. If an arbitrary constant is introduced then use the given conditions to find it.

Example 2.6

The retardation of a particle moving with speed v ms^{-1} at time t s is $3v^3$ ms^{-2}. When $t = 0$, $v = 2$ and the particle is passing through the fixed point O. Find

(a) the displacement of the particle at any subsequent time,

(b) the speed of the particle when its displacement from O is x m.

In this case the acceleration is negative and the equation of motion is

$$\frac{dv}{dt} = -3v^3,$$

carrying out the separation of variables as in step (i) gives

$$\int \frac{dv}{v^3} = -3 \int dt.$$

Integrating the left-hand side from $v = 2$ to $v = v$ and the right-hand side from $t = 0$ to $t = t$ gives

$$\frac{1}{2}\left(\frac{1}{v^2} - \frac{1}{4}\right) = 3t.$$

Solving for v in terms of t gives

$$v = \frac{2}{\sqrt{1 + 24t}}.$$

Replacing v by $\frac{dx}{dt}$ as in step (ii) gives

$$\frac{dx}{dt} = \frac{2}{\sqrt{1 + 24\,t}}.$$

Integrating this equation from $t = 0$ to $t = t$ gives, using $x = 0$ for $t = 0$,

$$x = \frac{\sqrt{1 + 24\,t}}{6} - \frac{1}{6}.$$

The above equation can be solved to give t in terms of x and the result substituted in the expression for $\frac{dx}{dt}$. Alternatively the acceleration can be written as $v\frac{dv}{dx}$ so that

$$v\frac{dv}{dx} = -3v^3$$

Separating the variables gives

$$\int \frac{dv}{v^2} = -3 \int dx$$

Integrating the left-hand side from $v = 2$ to $v = v$ and the right-hand side from $x = 0$ to $x = x$ shows that

$$\frac{1}{v} - \frac{1}{2} = 3x.$$

Solving for v in terms of x gives $\quad v = \dfrac{2}{1 + 6x}.$

Exercises 2.2

Questions 1 to 5 refer to a particle P moving along the x axis with acceleration a ms^{-2} in the positive x direction, x m denotes its displacement from the origin at time t s and v ms^{-1} its velocity in the positive x direction at that time.

1   $a = -6v$, $x = 3$ and $v = 5$ for $t = 0$.   Find x in terms of t.

2   $a = \dfrac{1}{v}$, $x = 4$ and $v = 3$ for $t = 0$.   Find v in terms of x.

3   $a = -\dfrac{v^2}{4}$, $x = 0$, $v = 2$ for $t = 0$.   Find v and t for $x = 8$.

4   $a = 4(2 - v)^2$, $x = 0$ and $v = 0$ for $t = 0$.   Find v in terms of t.

5   $a = -2\sqrt{v}$, $x = 0$ and $v = 4$ for $t = 0$.   Find the time taken to come to rest and the distance travelled in that time.

6   The retardation of a particle moving in a straight line is proportional to the cube of its speed. The speed of the particle drops from 10 ms^{-1} to 5 ms^{-1} in 9 seconds, find the distance travelled in this time.

7   The acceleration of a particle moving in a straight line is inversely proportional to its speed. The speed of the particle increases from 5 ms^{-1} to 15 ms^{-1} in 1 minute. Show that the distance travelled in this time is 650 m.

8   The retardation of a particle moving on a straight line is proportional to the n th power of its speed. Show that for $n < 2$ the particle only moves a finite distance.

2.3   Modelling resistance to moving bodies

Most problems on moving bodies relate to motion in air or (for boats and ships) a fluid such as water where the resistance of the fluid has a major effect on the resulting motion. The problem of the resistance (or drag) of a fluid is a rather complicated one and can essentially only be found by experiment. In modelling motion it is necessary to assume, on the basis of experimental results, particular forms for air or water resistance. Apart from these assumptions being reasonably consistent with experiment they have, in order to obtain reasonably simple results, to be such that the resulting mathematical problem is fairly simple (i.e. the integrations have to be easy). In real situations this latter assumption is not particularly necessary as numerical methods can be used when difficulties arise. Experimental evidence is available for falling bodies and for vehicles such as cars and aeroplanes.

Falling bodies

Though the bodies are modelled as particles the air resistance assumed is that experienced by a falling sphere. Experimental evidence has shown that for a moving sphere the form of resistance depends on the product du where d m denotes the diameter of the sphere and u ms^{-1} denotes its speed. The experimental results show that the resistance R in newtons is given by

$$R = 1.66 \times 10^{-4} du \quad \text{for } du < 10^{-5}$$
$$R = 0.2\, d^2 u^2 \quad \text{for } 10^{-2} < du < 1.$$

It is not possible from the experimental evidence to infer that a power law is valid for $10^{-5} < du < 10^{-2}$ and a combination of the two expressions might be more appropriate. The main conclusion from the above is that the air resistance is only directly proportional to speed for extremely small particles and/or very low speeds.

Assuming that resistance is proportional to the square of the speed appears to be a more valid assumption. The mathematics associated with resistance directly proportional to speed is however much simpler than that for other laws and this linear law is therefore often used as a first approximation.

Moving vehicles

Experiments show that for most purposes it may be assumed that the resistance on a moving vehicle can be written as $\frac{1}{2}\rho C_D AV^2$, where ρ is the density of the surrounding medium, V is the speed of the vehicle, A is the cross sectional area perpendicular to the fluid flow and C_D is the drag coefficient and is experimentally determined. In the 1920s the drag coefficient of a car was about 0.5, these days most drag coefficients for cars are lower than 0.4 with some being lower than 0.3.

For a car there is an additional element of resistance, known as the rolling resistance, which is primarily due to friction at the tyres. For relatively low speeds this can often be assumed to be either constant or directly proportional to speed.

Terminal speed

If the total force acting on a particle of mass m is $m f(v)$ then

$$\frac{dv}{dt} = f(v).$$

In many cases of resisted motion the function f has the following properties
(i)   there is one, and only one, positive value V of v such that $f(v) = 0$,
(ii) for $v > V$, $f < 0$,
(iii) for $v < V$, $f > 0$.

If at some time $v = u$ ($> V$) then v would be decreasing and would continue to do so until $v = V$ and as the derivative is then zero v would then stay constant. Similarly at some time $v = w$ ($< V$) then v would be increasing and would continue to do so until v = V and as the derivative is then zero v would then stay constant. Therefore in both instances the speed would tend to the constant value V. This value is known as the terminal (limiting) speed and is the speed when the total force acting is zero.

2.4 Problems involving resisted motion

Possibly one of the most important things to do when trying to solve problems involving resisted motion is, as stated in section 5.1 of M1, to pick a reference direction and find the component of force in that direction. It also helps to have a sketch with all the forces acting marked on it.

Sometimes in problems you may be told that the resistance is proportional to some power of the velocity but the constant of proportionality is not given. In such cases you will be given some other information, such as the terminal speed, which will determine the constant of proportionality.

Example 2.7

The resistive force acting on a particle of mass 0.2 kg and moving along a straight line is proportional to the speed of the particle and such that the particle experiences a resistance of 20 N when moving with speed 10 ms^{-1}. Find the time taken for the speed to drop from 10 ms^{-1} to 5 ms^{-1}.

The reference direction is taken in the direction of the initial velocity as shown in the diagram and the velocity of the particle at time t s after its speed is 10 ms^{-1} is denoted by v ms^{-1}.

The resistance will be assumed to be kv N, where k is a constant. This is equal to 20 N when $v = 10$ so that $k = 2$. The equation of motion is therefore

$$0.2 \frac{dv}{dt} = -2v,$$

i.e.

$$\frac{dv}{dt} = -10v.$$

This can be solved by separation of variables or, as mentioned above, by making the trial substitution $v = ae^{mt}$, this gives

$$mae^{mt} = -10ae^{mt},$$

so that $m = 10$ and $v = ae^{-10t}$. Substituting $v = 10$ for $t = 0$ gives $a = 10$ and $v = 10e^{-10t}$. The speed is 5 ms^{-1} when

$$10e^{-10t} = 5,$$

i.e.
$$-10t = \ln\left(\frac{1}{2}\right),$$

giving
$$t = \frac{\ln 2}{10}.$$

Example 2.8

A stone of mass m kg is thrown upwards with speed 2 ms^{-1}. The air resistance, when the stone is moving with speed v ms^{-1} is $\frac{1}{2}mvg$ newtons. Find, in terms of g, the time taken to reach the highest point.

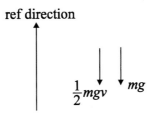

The forces acting on the stone during the period that it is rising are shown in the diagram and the reference direction is taken upwards. The equation of motion is
$$m\frac{dv}{dt} = -mg - \frac{1}{2}mvg,$$

or
$$\frac{dv}{dt} = -g\left(1 + \frac{1}{2}v\right).$$

Separating the variables as in step (i) gives
$$\frac{1}{\left(1 + \frac{1}{2}v\right)}\frac{dv}{dt} = -g,$$

and therefore
$$\int\frac{dv}{1 + \frac{1}{2}v} = -g\int dt.$$

At the point of greatest height the speed will be zero and therefore integrating the left-hand side from $v = 2$ to $v = 0$ and the right-hand side from $t = 0$ to $t = t$ gives
$$-2\ln(2) = -gt,$$

so
$$t = \frac{2\ln 2}{g}.$$

Example 2.9

Find, for the problem of Example 4.8, (a) an expression for the height travelled in a time t s after projection, (b) the greatest height reached, (c) an expression for speed in terms of height.

In order to find the displacement it is necessary to find v in terms of t, one way of doing this is to integrate the left- hand side of

$$\int \frac{dv}{1+\frac{1}{2}v} = -g\int dt.$$

from $v = 2$ to $v = v$ and the right hand side from $t = 0$ to $t = t$.
Alternatively v can be found by solving

$$\frac{dv}{dt} = -g\left(1+\frac{1}{2}v\right),$$

as an equation with constant coefficients. Trying $v = c$, where c is a constant gives $c = -2$ so that a particular integral is -2. The homogeneous equation is

$$\frac{dv}{dt} = -\frac{g}{2}v,$$

making the trial substitution $v = ae^{mt}$ gives $m = -\frac{g}{2}$ so that the general solution is

$$v = -2 + ae^{\frac{-gt}{2}} \quad \text{where } a \text{ is a constant.}$$

Substituting $v = 2$ for $t = 0$ gives $a = 4$ and

$$v = \frac{dx}{dt} = -2 + 4e^{\frac{-gt}{2}}.$$

Integrating this equation from $t = 0$ to $t = t$ gives

$$x = -2t - \frac{8}{g}(e^{\frac{-gt}{2}} - 1).$$

The time to maximum height is, from the previous Example, or by setting $v = 0$ in the expression for v, $\frac{2\ln 2}{g}$. Substituting this value for the time in the expression for x gives the maximum height as $\frac{4}{g}(1 - \ln 2)$.

It is not possible to invert the expression for x to express t in terms of x but it is possible to express t in terms of v to give $t = -\frac{2}{g}\ln\left(\frac{v}{4}+\frac{1}{2}\right)$ and substituting in the expression for x gives

$$x = \frac{4}{g} \ln\left(\frac{v}{4} + \frac{1}{2}\right) - \frac{8}{g}(v - 2).$$

In this problem writing the acceleration as $v\dfrac{dv}{dx}$ leads to some algebra which is not directly covered in your course and the method cannot be used to find a relationship between v and x.

Example 2.10

A stone of mass m kg is thrown upwards with speed 2 ms^{-1}. The air resistance, when the stone is moving with speed v ms^{-1} is $\frac{1}{4}mv^2g$ newtons. Find, in terms of g, the maximum height reached. Find also the maximum speed attained on the downward path and the speed with which the stone returns to the initial point.

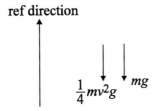

The forces acting on the stone during the period that it is rising are shown in the diagram and the reference direction is taken upwards. The equation of motion is

$$m\frac{dv}{dt} = -mg - \frac{1}{4}mv^2g,$$

or

$$\frac{dv}{dt} = -g\left(1 + \frac{1}{4}v^2\right).$$

In this problem, since the height is required, it seems more appropriate to write the acceleration as $v\dfrac{dv}{dx}$ so that

$$v\frac{dv}{dx} = -g\left(1 + \frac{1}{4}v^2\right)$$

Separating the variables and integrating with respect to x gives

$$\int \frac{vdv}{1 + \frac{1}{4}v^2} = -g\int dx.$$

At the point of greatest height the speed will be zero and therefore integrating the left-hand side from $v = 2$ to $v = 0$ and the right-hand side from $x = 0$ to $x = x$ gives

$$\int\limits_{2}^{0} \frac{v\,dv}{1+\dfrac{1}{4}v^2} = -gx$$

Carrying out the integration gives

$$2\ln\left(1+\frac{1}{4}v^2\right)\Bigg|_{v=2}^{v=0} = -2\ln(2) = -gx$$

so

$$x = \frac{2\ln 2}{g}.$$

The downward motion has now to be investigated and the reference direction is now taken to be downwards from the point of maximum height. The forces acting on the stone are shown in the diagram.

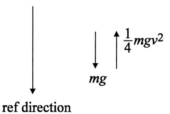

ref direction

The equation of motion is

$$mv\frac{dv}{dx} = mg - mg\,\frac{v^2}{4}\,,$$

or

$$v\frac{dv}{dx} = g\left(1-\frac{v^2}{4}\right).$$

The right hand side vanishes for $v = 2$ and therefore the maximum speed that could be attained on the downward path is $2\ \text{ms}^{-1}$.

Separating the variables and integrating the left-hand side from $v = 0$ to $v = w$, where $w\ \text{ms}^{-1}$ denotes the maximum speed of the stone, and the right-hand side from $x = 0$ to $x = \dfrac{2\ln 2}{g}$ gives

$$\int\limits_{0}^{w} \frac{v\,dv}{1-\dfrac{1}{4}v^2} = 2\ln 2.$$

Carrying out the integration gives

$$-2\ln\left(1-\frac{1}{4}v^2\right)\Bigg|_{v=0}^{v=w} = -2\ln\left(1-\frac{1}{4}w^2\right) = 2\ln 2,$$

giving

$$\ln\left(1-\frac{1}{4}w^2\right) = -\ln 2 \text{ so that } 1-\frac{1}{4}w^2 = \frac{1}{2} \text{ and } w = \sqrt{2}\,.$$

Exercises 2.3

1   A particle of mass 0.5 kg moving with speed v ms^{-1} is resisted by a force of $2v$ newtons. Find the time taken for its speed to reduce from 20 ms^{-1} to 2 ms^{-1}.

2   A particle of mass 0.2 kg is projected with initial speed 6 ms^{-1} along a rough horizontal table, the coefficient of friction being 0.5. The particle is also subject to air resistance which, when it is moving with speed v ms^{-1}, is equal to $0.1v$ newtons.

   Find the time taken for the particle to come to rest.

3   A particle subject to a resistance proportional to the square of its speed has its speed reduced from 8 ms^{-1} to 4 ms^{-1} in 6 seconds. Find the distance it travels in that time.

4   An aeroplane of mass 20 tonnes takes off under a constant thrust of 250 kN. The drag on the aeroplane when moving with speed v ms^{-1} is $10v^2$ N. Its take off speed is 90 ms^{-1}. Find the minimum length of runway.

5   A car of mass m moves under the action of a constant driving force F and a resistance, which when the car's speed is v, is mkv. Find the maximum speed that the car can attain and the time taken, from rest, before three quarters of this speed is attained.

6   A parachutist jumps from a balloon. The air resistance is assumed to be proportional to the speed of the parachutist and his terminal speed is 5 ms^{-1}. Find his speed after 0.5 s and the distance he has dropped in that time.

7   If the resistance in the previous question is assumed to be proportional to the square of the speed, with the terminal velocity being unchanged, find the speed after the parachutist has been dropping for 1 s.

8   A particle of mass 0.5 kg moves in a straight line under the action of a resistive force of magnitude $0.4(1 + v^2)$ newtons when the speed of the particle is v ms^{-1}. Show that it is reduced to rest from a speed of 4 ms^{-1} in time $1.25 \tan^{-1} 4$ s.

Miscellaneous Exercises 2

1   The engine of a powerboat is shut off when its speed is 12 ms^{-1} and the water drag is assumed to produce a retardation of $0.1\, v^2$ ms^{-2} when the boat is moving with speed v ms^{-1}.

   (a)   Write down the differential equation governing the motion and find an expression for the time taken for the speed of the boat to drop to v ms^{-1}.

   (b)   Explain, by considering the time taken to come to rest, why the model of retardation chosen is not particularly realistic and suggest an alternative formula for retardation which may be more suitable. (There is no need to carry out any calculations using your suggested retardation.)

2   A particle P of mass 0.3 kg moves along a horizontal straight line. The particle is acted upon by a horizontal resistive force of magnitude $1.2v^{n+1}$ newtons ($n > 0$) where v ms^{-1} is the speed of P at time t s. At time $t = 0$ the particle is at a point O and moving with speed u ms^{-1}.

(a) (i) Obtain the differential equation relating $\dfrac{dv}{dt}$ and v.

(ii) Solve this differential equation to find an expression for v in terms of u, t and n.

(b) For the case $n = 3$

(i) obtain, in terms of u and x, an expression for v at a point a distance x metres from O,

(ii) determine, in terms of u and x, the rate at which work is being done against the resistance when P is x metres from O.

3   The non-gravitational resistance to the motion of a car of mass 1000 kg moving with speed v ms^{-1} is known to be of the form $(kv + 0.05\,kv^2)$ N, where k is a constant. When the car's engine is working at a rate of 11.25 kW the car can move at a steady speed of 25 ms^{-1} on a horizontal road.

(a) Find the value of k.

(b) Find the rate at which the car's engine works when the car is moving at a steady speed of 15 ms^{-1} up a hill inclined at an angle $\sin^{-1}\left(\dfrac{1}{49}\right)$ to the horizontal.

(c) When the car is moving with speed 25 ms^{-1} on a horizontal road the engine is switched off. Show that the speed v ms^{-1} of the car, after travelling a distance of x m after the engine has been switched off, satisfies the differential equation

$$2500\frac{dv}{dx} = -20 - v.$$

Solve this differential equation to find the distance travelled before the car's speed falls to 5 ms^{-1}.

4   A particle of mass 0.4 kg is projected vertically upwards with a speed of 30 ms^{-1}. Verify that the time taken to reach its greatest height is more than 3 s.

In an experiment when the particle was projected as above it was found that the actual time to reach its greatest height was 2 s. Assuming that this difference in times is due to the existence of air resistance which is directly proportional to the speed of the particle show that the speed v ms^{-1} of the particle at time t s after projection satisfies a differential equation of the form

$$\frac{dv}{dt} = -9.8 - kv,$$

where k is a constant. Solve this differential equation to determine v in terms of k and t. Verify that a value of 0.4 for k produces good agreement with observation. Use this value of k to find the air resistance when the particle is moving at a speed of 12 ms^{-1}.

5 In a particular model of the braking effect of a car the retardation of the car, when moving with speed v ms^{-1}, is $\frac{600}{v+175}$ ms^{-2}. Find the time taken for a car to stop from a speed of 25 ms^{-1} and the distance travelled in that time.

6 A particle of mass 0.2 kg moves in a horizontal straight line under the action of a resistive force proportional to its speed. The force is 2 N when the car is moving with speed 10 ms^{-1}. Given that the speed is v ms^{-1} at time t seconds show that

$$\frac{dv}{dt} = -v.$$

Find (i) the time taken for the speed to decrease from 4 ms^{-1} to 2 ms^{-1},

(ii) the distance travelled during this period.

7 A rocket of mass m is projected vertically upwards from a point on the earth's surface and it moves along a straight line which passes through the centre O of the earth. When the rocket reaches a distance b from O its fuel has been exhausted and its speed is u. It then continues under the action of the earth's gravity only.

(a) Assuming that the gravitational force on the rocket has the constant value mg,

(i) find the speed of the rocket when at a distance x ($> b$) from O,

(ii) describe the subsequent motion of the rocket.

(b) Assuming that the gravitational force acting on the rocket when it is at a distance $x(> b)$ from O is $\frac{mk}{x^2}$ directed towards O, where k is a constant,

(i) find the speed of the rocket when it is at a distance $x(> b)$ from O,

(ii) describe the subsequent motion when $u^2 < \frac{2k}{b}$,

(iii) describe the subsequent motion when $u^2 > \frac{2k}{b}$.

8 The maximum speed of a car is V and the resistance to its motion varies as the square of its speed. If its engine works at a constant maximum rate the car attains a speed of $\frac{1}{2} V$ from rest in a distance a. If the engine exerts a constant maximum tractive force the car attains the speed $\frac{1}{2} V$ from rest in a distance b.

Show that $\dfrac{a}{b} = \dfrac{2\ln\frac{8}{7}}{3\ln\frac{4}{3}}.$

9 A particle is projected vertically upwards in a medium in which at any instant the resistance to its motion is mk times the square of its speed at that instant. Deduce that the greatest height H achieved by the particle is related to its initial speed u by

$$u^2 = \frac{g}{k}(e^{2kH} - 1)$$

Find the corresponding relation between H and the speed U of the particle when it returns to its starting point. Hence show that

$$U = u\,e^{-kH}.$$

10 A truck of mass 1000 kg starting from rest, runs down a slope of inclination $\sin^{-1}\dfrac{5}{49}$. It is subject to a frictional force of $(100v + 500)$ N, where v is its speed in metres per second. Show that the equation of motion of the truck is

$$\frac{dv}{dt} = \frac{1}{2} - \frac{v}{10}.$$

Deduce that the speed cannot exceed 5 ms^{-1}. By solving this differential equation show that t s after its release from rest the truck is travelling at a speed of

$$5\left(1 - e^{\frac{t}{10}}\right) \text{ ms}^{-1}.$$

What is the distance travelled by the truck in time t s?

Show that it will have travelled $5(10\ln 10 - 9)$ m when its speed reaches 0.9 of its maximum speed.

11 A body of mass 240 kg is dropped by parachute with negligible initial speed.

Whilst the parachute is opening the body is subject at time t s to a resistance due to the atmosphere of $40v$ N where v ms^{-1} is its speed at that time. Show that whilst the parachute is opening

$$6\frac{dv}{dt} = 6g - v.$$

If the parachute is fully open after 6 s, prove that the speed of the body will then be $6g(1 - e^{-1})$ ms^{-1}.

Find an expression for the distance fallen by the body in time t s ($t \le 6$).

Show that the body has fallen through a distance of $36ge^{-1}$ whilst the parachute is opening.

12 A particle of mass m moves along the x-axis under the action of a force $-\dfrac{2mn^2a^2x}{(a^2+x^2)^2}$ in the x direction, where n and a are constants and x is the displacement of the particle from O. Show, or verify, that the speed v of the particle when its displacement from the origin is x is such that

$$v^2 - \frac{2n^2a^2}{(a^2+x^2)} \quad \text{is constant.}$$

(a) The particle is projected from $x = 2a$ with speed u in the negative x direction. Find

   (i) the least value of u so that the particle can escape to infinity,

   (ii) the value of x at the point where the particle first comes to instantaneous rest for the case when $u = \dfrac{n}{\sqrt{5}}$.

(b) The particle is projected from infinity so that at $x = 0$ its kinetic energy is $3mn^2$ and it then receives an impulse so that its kinetic energy becomes $3pmn^2$, where p is a constant. Find

   (i) the speed of projection,

   (ii) the range of values of p such that the subsequent motion is confined to a finite region of the x-axis.

Chapter 3

Simple Harmonic Motion

After working through this chapter you should

- know what is meant by simple harmonic motion (S.H.M.) and be able to recognise problems on simple harmonic motion,
- be able to solve kinematic and dynamic problems involving simple harmonic motion,
- be able to refine the problems to take into account damping.

3.1   Basic ideas

Simple harmonic motion is a particular motion on a straight line and is possibly best understood by looking at a couple of examples.

As the first example we consider a particle P moving on the x axis so that its displacement x metres from the origin at time t seconds is given by

$$x = 2 \sin t.$$

The diagram shows the behaviour of x with t.

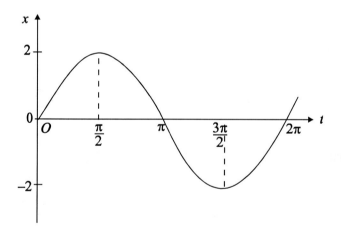

The velocity $v \text{ ms}^{-1}$ of the particle in the direction of increasing x is therefore given by

$$v = \frac{\mathrm{d}x}{\mathrm{d}t} = 2 \cos t.$$

For $t = 0$ the particle is at the origin and has a velocity of 2 ms^{-1} in the positive x direction. Therefore P will start moving in the direction of increasing x. The maximum value of x occurs when sin t first reaches its maximum value of 1 and this occurs when $t = \dfrac{\pi}{2}$. The maximum value of x is therefore 2. Since $t = \dfrac{\pi}{2}$, the velocity of P is zero when x has its maximum value i.e. P is at its maximum distance from the origin. As t continues to increase x starts decreasing and P reaches the origin when sin $t = 0$ i.e. $t = \pi$. At this instant $v = -2$ so that P is moving in the negative x direction with speed 2 ms^{-1}. For $t > \pi$, sin t is negative and x continues to decrease until sin t reaches its minimum value of -1 and this occurs when $t = \dfrac{3\pi}{2}$. At this time $v = 0$ so that P is instantaneously at rest.

For $t > \dfrac{3\pi}{2}$, v is positive so P moves in the positive x direction and reaches the origin when sin $t = 0$, i.e. $t = 2\pi$. At this time $v = 2$ so that P is moving with speed 2 ms^{-1} in the positive x direction. This is exactly the same situation as that when $t = 0$ and therefore the motion is repeated in that, for example, in a further time of $\dfrac{\pi}{2}$ seconds P is again at its maximum distance from the origin. The stages in the motion are therefore

(i) P travels from the origin to the point A in the following diagram where $x = 2$, where it comes to instantaneous rest,

(ii) P travels from A to the origin, where $v = -2$,

(iii) P travels from the origin to the point B where $x = -2$, where it comes to instantaneous rest,

(iv) P travels from B to the origin, where $v = 2$.

The cycle then repeats itself and the motion is therefore an oscillatory one, the total time taken for a complete cycle being 2π s, this is the period of the oscillation. The time taken for each of the above stages is $\dfrac{\pi}{2}$ s, i.e. a quarter of the period.

As the second example we consider a particle P moving on the x axis so that its displacement x metres from the origin at time t seconds is given by

$$x = 4 \cos 3t.$$

The following diagram shows the behaviour of x with t.

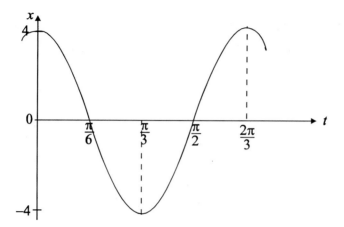

The velocity v ms^{-1} of the particle in the direction of increasing x is therefore given by

$$v = \frac{dx}{dt} = -12 \sin 3t.$$

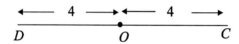

For $t = 0$ the particle is at the point C where $x = 4$ and is instantaneously at rest. As t increases $\cos 3t$ decreases therefore P will start moving in the direction of decreasing x and reaches the origin when $\cos 3t = 0$. This occurs when $3t = \frac{\pi}{2}$ i.e. when $t = \frac{\pi}{6}$.

At this time $v = -12$ and P starts moving along the negative x axis and continues to move until $\cos 3t$ reaches its minimum value of -1. This occurs when $3t = \pi$, i.e. $t = \frac{\pi}{3}$ (i.e. t has increased by a further $\frac{\pi}{6}$). At this time $v = 0$ so that P is instantaneously at rest at the point D where $x = -4$. For $t > \frac{\pi}{3}$, v is positive and so P moves in the positive x direction and reaches the origin when $\cos 3t = 0$, i.e. $3t = \frac{3\pi}{2}$ and $t = \frac{\pi}{2}$ (with t showing a further increase of $\frac{\pi}{6}$). At this time $v = 12$ so that, at the origin, P is moving with speed 12 ms^{-1} in the positive x direction. It therefore starts moving along the positive x axis until $\cos 3t$ reaches its maximum value of 1; this occurs when $t = \frac{2\pi}{3}$ (i.e. t has increased by a further $\frac{\pi}{6}$). At this time the particle is again instantaneously at rest at C. This is exactly the same situation as that when $t = 0$ and therefore the cycle is repeated. The stages in the motion are therefore

(i) P travels from the point C, where $x = 4$, shown in the diagram to the origin,

(ii) P travels from the origin to the point D where $x = -4$,

(iii) P travels from D to the origin,

(iv) P continues from the origin back to the point C where $v = 0$.

The cycle then repeats itself and the motion is therefore an oscillatory one, the total time taken for a complete cycle being $\frac{2\pi}{3}$ s; this is the period of the oscillation. The time taken for each of the above stages is $\frac{\pi}{6}$s, i.e. a quarter of the period.

Both the above are examples of simple harmonic motion (often abbreviated to S.H.M.) with centre O (this is the point midway between the extreme positions). The most general form of simple harmonic motion with centre O is defined by

$$x = a \sin (\omega t + \varepsilon),$$

where a, ω and ε are constants with a being positive. In the first example $a = 2$, $\omega = 1$ and $\varepsilon = 0$, whereas in the second example $a = 4$, $\omega = 3$ and $\varepsilon = \frac{\pi}{2}$.

The general form of x is shown for $\varepsilon < \frac{\pi}{2}$ in the following diagram.

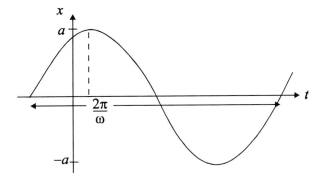

The velocity v in the positive x direction is given by

$$v = \frac{dx}{dt} = a\omega \cos(\omega t + \varepsilon)$$

The motion is periodic, the period being $\frac{2\pi}{\omega}$. If the time T for one oscillation is $\frac{2\pi}{\omega}$ then the number of oscillations per unit time is $\frac{1}{T} = \frac{\omega}{2\pi}$, this is called the frequency of the oscillation. In S.I. units the unit of frequency is the hertz (Hz) with one hertz being one oscillation (or cycle) per second. Since ωt is an angle measured in radians the units of ω in the S.I. system are rads^{-1}. ω is known as the circular frequency, this is not a particularly obvious term and its use stems from the fact that there is a relationship between S.H.M. and circular motion. This is discussed in section 4.5.

The particle is furthest from O when $\sin (\omega t + \varepsilon) = \pm 1$ and therefore $x = \pm a$, so that the maximum distance from the origin is a which is called the amplitude of the motion. When $\sin(\omega t + \varepsilon) = 1$, $\cos(\omega t + \varepsilon) = 0$, so the particle is instantaneously at rest at the extreme points.

The particle passes through the origin when $\sin(\omega t + \varepsilon) = 0$ and at these times $\cos(\omega t + \varepsilon) = \pm 1$ so that at the origin the speed has its maximum value of $a\omega$.

You can see from the symmetry of the sine function that the time to travel between a maximum point (i.e. an extreme point) and the origin is a quarter of the period. .

Simple harmonic motion of amplitude a and centre O is therefore a motion between the point A where $x = a$ and the point B where $x = -a$.

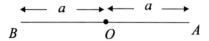

A particle P moving to the right in the above diagram at a point in-between A and B, will come to instantaneous rest at A and then start moving to the left and continue to do so until it reaches B where it again comes to instantaneous rest before moving to the right to its initial position.

A particle P moving to the left in the above diagram at a point in-between A and B, will come to instantaneous rest at B and then start moving to the right and continue to do so until it reaches A where it again comes to instantaneous rest before moving to the left to its initial position.

It can be very useful in solving problems involving S.H.M. to use a simple diagram like the one above to visualise what is happening. For problems where the direction of motion of the particle has to be taken into account such a diagram is almost vital.

Though the form $x = a \sin(\omega t + \varepsilon)$ is the easiest one from which to see the general behaviour of simple harmonic motion it is not the best form to use to try and determine x given conditions at a specific value of t. In this case it is generally easier to use the general solution of the simple harmonic equation in the form $x = A \cos \omega t + B \sin \omega t$. This form can also be obtained from expanding $\sin(\omega t + \varepsilon)$.

If a particle is at the origin for $t = 0$ then $A = 0$ so that $x = B \sin \omega t$, the maximum magnitude of x is $|B|$ and this by definition of the amplitude is a, therefore $B = \pm a$ and $x = \pm a \sin \omega t$. Differentiating this gives $\dfrac{dx}{dt} = \pm a\omega \cos \omega t$ so the plus sign corresponds to a particle moving to the right at the origin and the minus sign corresponds to a particle moving to the left at the origin.

The form $x = \pm a \sin \omega t$ therefore represents a motion when the particle is at the origin at time $t = 0$, the plus and minus signs corresponding to a particle moving in the direction of increasing x or in the direction of decreasing x, respectively, at the origin.

If a particle is at one of the extreme points at $t = 0$ then it will be at rest and since

$\dfrac{dx}{dt} = -\omega A \sin \omega t + \omega B \cos \omega t$ this means that $B = 0$. Therefore $A = a$ if the particle

is initially at $x = a$ and $A = -a$ if the particle is initially at $x = -a$.

The form $x = \pm a \sin \omega t$ therefore represents a motion when the particle is at one of the extreme points $x = \pm a$ at time $t = 0$, the plus and minus signs corresponding, respectively, to the extreme positions $x = a$ and $x = -a$.

There are many examples in "real-life" where the motion is simple harmonic. Particular examples are the tip of the needle in a sewing machine, the motion of a cork pushed down gently in water, the motion of a particle made to oscillate at the end of a spring, the variation in the level of the tide in a harbour, the motion of a point on the blade of an electric jig saw.

The motion of the weight at the end of a clock pendulum and the up and down motion of the piston in the engine of a car are both approximately simple harmonic.

Alternative definitions

The above definition of S.H.M. is the one that shows most clearly the nature of the motion. There are alternative definitions that you may come across and you need to be able to recognise these. These alternatives can all be obtained from the above form.

If $x = a \sin (\omega t + \varepsilon)$ then $v = a\omega \cos (\omega t + \varepsilon) =$ and therefore
$$v^2 = a^2 \omega^2 \cos^2 (\omega t + \varepsilon).$$
Since $\cos^2 (\omega t + \varepsilon) = 1 - \sin^2 (\omega t + \varepsilon)$ the expression for v^2 can be rewritten as
$$v^2 = a^2 \omega^2 (1 - \sin^2 (\omega t + \varepsilon)).$$
and substituting for $\sin (\omega t + \varepsilon)$ in terms of x gives
$$v^2 = (\omega^2 a^2 - x^2)$$

This expression for v in terms of x is an alternative way of defining S.H.M. and in order to confirm this it is necessary to show that the general solution for x is of the form

$a \sin (\omega t + \varepsilon)$. The easiest way of doing this is to write x as $a \sin \theta$ so that, using the chain rule,

$$v = \frac{dx}{dt} = a \cos \theta \frac{d\theta}{dt}$$

Substituting for x and v in terms of θ gives
$$\left(\frac{d\theta}{dt} \right) = \omega^2,$$

so that
$$\frac{d\theta}{dt} = \pm \omega$$

Integrating this gives
$$\theta = \omega t + \text{constant},$$
so that x will be of the form $a \sin(\omega t + \varepsilon)$.

An alternative method of obtaining x is to take the square root of the expression for v^2 and integrate by separating the variables as in Example 2.4.

If $x = a \sin(\omega t + \varepsilon)$, then
$$\frac{d^2 x}{dt^2} = -a\omega^2 \sin(\omega t + \varepsilon)$$

and substituting for $\sin(\omega t + \varepsilon)$ in terms of x gives
$$\frac{d^2 x}{dt^2} = -\omega^2 x$$

This gives a further definition of S.H.M. i.e. that the motion of any particle whose displacement satisfies the above differential equation is simple harmonic. To confirm this it is necessary to show that the general solution of the above equation is of the form $x = a \sin(\omega t + \varepsilon)$, This has already been shown at the end of Example 1.5 where n is used instead of ω.

For $x > 0$ the acceleration is in the negative x direction i.e. towards the origin and for $x < 0$ the acceleration is in the positive x direction i.e. again towards the origin. Therefore very often the differential equation is stated in the alternative verbal form "the acceleration is always directed towards the centre and directly proportional to the distance from it".

Since force is mass times acceleration this latter form can be restated as "simple harmonic motion is produced by a force acting towards the centre and directly proportional to the distance from it".

The differential equation can also be obtained by differentiating $v^2 = \omega^2(a^2 - x^2)$ with respect to x and using the identity
$$v \frac{dv}{dx} = \frac{d^2 x}{dt^2}.$$

Equivalently using the above identity in the differential equation and integrating with respect to x gives
$$v^2 = \omega^2 x^2 + \text{constant},$$
and writing the constant in the form $\omega^2 a^2$ gives $v^2 = \omega^2(a^2 - x^2)$.

These results can be summarised as follows:

Summary of basic formulae

If a particle describes S.H.M. along the x axis about the origin O with period $\dfrac{2\pi}{\omega}$ and amplitude a then

$$\text{Period} \;=\; \frac{2\pi}{\omega}$$

$$\text{Frequency} \;=\; \frac{\omega}{2\pi}$$

$$x \;=\; a \sin(\omega t + \varepsilon),$$
$$x \;=\; A \cos \omega t + B \sin \omega t,$$

(this form is the most useful one if conditions are given for $t = 0$)

$$v^2 \;=\; \omega^2\left(a^2 - x^2\right),$$

$$\frac{d^2 x}{dt^2} \;=\; -\,\omega^2 x,$$

where x and v denote the displacement and the velocity of the particle at time t.

Each one of the last four equations defines simple harmonic motion and any one of these equations can be obtained from any of the others. These are the **fundamental formulae for S.H.M.** and you should commit them to memory. Other basic results for motion with centre O are :

> Maximum speed is at the centre and equal to $a\omega$.
>
> Distance between extreme points $= 2a$.
>
> Displacement of a particle at O for $t = 0$ is $\pm a \sin \omega t$.
>
> Displacement of a particle at $x = \pm a$ for $t = 0$ is $\pm \cos \omega t$.

Centre not at the origin

The centre of the motion need not be the origin but could, for example, be the point $x = b$.

If X denotes the displacement of the particle from $x = b$, then, by definition of S.H.M, $X = a \sin(\omega t + \varepsilon)$ However, as you can see from the diagram $x = X + b$ so that

$$x \;=\; b + a \sin(\omega t + \varepsilon)$$

and the other results become

$$v^2 \;=\; +\,\omega^2\left(a^2 - (x - b)^2\right),$$

$$\frac{d^2 x}{dt^2} \;=\; \omega^2(x - b).$$

Maximum speed is at the centre and equal to $a\omega$.

Distance between extreme points $= 2a$.

Displacement of a particle at the centre for $t = 0$ is $b \pm a \sin \omega t$.

Displacement of a particle at $x = \pm a + b$ for $t = 0$ is $b \pm a \cos \omega t$.

3.2   Kinematic problems

The simplest problems are kinematic ones when you are given that the motion is simple harmonic and some information and you are required to find further information.

In the following numerical examples it will be assumed that x m and b m denote, respectively, the displacements at time t s of a particle P and of the centre of the oscillation, from a fixed origin O. The amplitude of any simple harmonic motion will be denoted by a m and the circular frequency by ω rads^{-1}.

The velocity at time t s of the particle is denoted by v ms^{-1}. The quantities x, b, a, v, t and ω are therefore pure numbers satisfying the above fundamental relations.

The basic unknowns are a and ω and the first step is to use the given information to find these.

Example 3.1

A particle describes S.H.M. with period π s and the distance between the extreme points of the motion is 4 m. Find the greatest speed of the particle and its speed when at a distance of 1 m from the centre of the oscillation.

Since the period π s it follows that $\dfrac{2\pi}{\omega} = \omega$ and therefore $\omega = 2$.

The distance between the extreme points is twice the amplitude and therefore $a = 2$. The maximum speed $a\omega$ and is therefore 4 ms^{-1}.

The speed when the distance of the particle from the centre is x m is found from the result $v^2 = \omega^2 \left(a^2 - x^2 \right)$. Substituting the values in this gives the speed as $2\sqrt{3}$ ms^{-1}.

Example 3.2

A particle moving in simple harmonic motion makes 4 oscillations per second and the distance between the extreme points of the motion is 0.3 m. Find the greatest acceleration of the particle.

The period of each oscillation is $\frac{1}{4}$ s and therefore $\frac{2\pi}{\omega} = \frac{1}{4}$ so that $\omega = 8\pi$.

The distance between the extreme points is twice the amplitude and therefore $a = 0.15$.

The acceleration is $-\omega^2 x$. The maximum acceleration will therefore be when x is greatest, i.e. at the extreme points. Therefore the maximum acceleration is $\omega^2 a$ and substituting the values found for ω and a gives the maximum acceleration as $9.6\pi^2$ ms^{-2}.

Example 3.3

The displacement x m of a particle at time t s is given by $x = 3\cos 2t + 4\sin 2t$. Find the amplitude and period of the oscillation.

The first step is to write the displacement in the form $a\sin(\omega t + \varepsilon)$. This latter form can be expanded as $a\sin \omega t \cos \varepsilon + a\cos \omega t \sin \varepsilon$.

The two forms will be the same provided that $\omega = 2$, $3 = a\sin \varepsilon$, $4 = a\cos \varepsilon$. Squaring and adding these last two equations gives $a = 5$ and therefore the amplitude is 5 m and the period π s.

Example 3.4

The greatest speed of a particle describing simple harmonic motion in a straight line is 10ms^{-1} and its speed when at a distance of 4 m from the centre of the oscillation is 6ms^{-1}. Find the period and amplitude of the oscillation.

It follows from the fact that the maximum speed is 10 ms^{-1} that
$$a\omega = 10,$$
also substituting $v = 6$ and $x = 4$ into $v^2 = \omega^2(a^2 - x^2)$, gives
$$36 = \omega^2 a^2 - \omega^2 16.$$
Substituting $a\omega = 10$ into this equation gives $\omega = 2$ and therefore the period is π s.
Since $\omega = 2$ it follows from $a\omega = 10$ that $a = 5$ and the amplitude is therefore 5 m.

Example 3.5

The speed of a particle describing simple harmonic motion in a straight line is 6 ms^{-1} when at a distance of 1 m from the centre of the oscillation and 2 ms^{-1} when at a distance of 3 m from the centre of the oscillation. Find the period and amplitude of the oscillation.

Substituting $v = 6$ and $x = 1$, into $v^2 = \omega^2 (a^2 - x^2)$, gives

$$36 = \omega^2 (a^2 - 1),$$

whilst substituting $v = 2$ and $x = 3$, into $v^2 = \omega^2 (a^2 - x^2)$, gives

$$4 = \omega^2 (a^2 - 9).$$

These are simultaneous equations for a and ω and dividing them to eliminate ω gives

$$9 = \frac{(a^2 - 1)}{(a^2 - 9)}.$$

Solving for a gives $a = \sqrt{10}$ giving the amplitude as $\sqrt{10}$ m. Substituting $a = \sqrt{10}$ in $36 = \omega^2 (a^2 - 1)$ shows that $\omega = 2$ and therefore the period is π s.

Example 3.6

A particle describes simple harmonic motion, centre O, with period 4 s and amplitude 5m. Given that the particle is at O at time $t = 0$ find its displacement from O at any subsequent time t s. Find also the time taken for the particle to travel (i) from O directly to the point C where $OC = 2.5$ m, (ii) from C directly to the point D where $CD = 1.5$ m.

Since the period is 4 s, $\dfrac{2\pi}{\omega} = 4$ and therefore $\omega = \dfrac{\pi}{2}$. The displacement is obtained by substituting $a = 5$ and $\omega = \dfrac{\pi}{2}$ in $x = a \sin \omega t$ giving

$$x = 5 \sin \frac{\pi}{2} t.$$

In problems involving time from point to point it is often helpful to draw a simple sketch, as follows, marking in the points.

$$O \xleftarrow{\quad 2.5 \text{ m} \quad} C \xleftarrow{1.5 \text{ m}} D$$

The value of t to reach C is found by substituting $x = 2.5$ in the above expression and solving for t, i.e.

$$2.5 = 5 \sin \frac{\pi}{2} t,$$

there are an infinite number of solutions but we only need the smallest since we only require the time to go directly to C and therefore $\dfrac{\pi}{2} t = \sin^{-1} \dfrac{1}{2} = \dfrac{\pi}{6}$ and therefore $t = \dfrac{1}{3}$.

The quickest way of finding the time to travel directly from C to D is to find the time from O to D and subtract from it the time from O to C. The time from O to D is found by solving

$$4 = 5 \sin \frac{\pi}{2} t$$

for t. Therefore $\dfrac{\pi}{2} t = \sin^{-1} 0.8 \ (= 0.927)$. It is very important to remember that the inverse sine has to be found in radians and this gives t to be approximately 0.59. Subtracting the time taken from O to C gives the time from C to D to be approximately 0.26 s.

Example 3.7

A particle describes simple harmonic motion, centre O, with period 6 s and amplitude 3m. Given that the particle is at rest at the point A on the positive x axis at time $t = 0$ find its displacement from O at any subsequent time t s. Find also the time taken for the particle to travel directly to the point C where C is between O and A and $OC = 2$m.

Since the period is 6s, $\dfrac{2\pi}{\omega} = 6$ and therefore $\omega = \dfrac{\pi}{3}$. Since the particle is at rest at A for

$t = 0$ then A is one of the extreme points of the motion. Therefore the displacement is obtained by substituting $a = 3$ and $\omega = \dfrac{\pi}{3}$ in $x = a \cos \omega t$ giving

$$x = 3 \cos \frac{\pi}{3} t.$$

The starting point and the point C are shown in the following sketch.

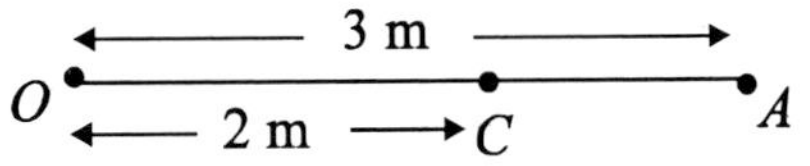

The value of t to reach C is found by substituting $x = 2$ in the above expression and solving for t, i.e.

$$2 = 3 \cos \frac{\pi}{3} t.$$

the smallest value of t is given by $\dfrac{\pi}{3} t = \cos^{-1} \dfrac{2}{3}$, and therefore $t = 0.8$.

Example 3.8

A particle describes simple harmonic motion, centre O of amplitude 3 m and passes through a point at a distance of 1.5 m from O on two successive occasions at 2 seconds apart. Find the two possible periods of oscillation.

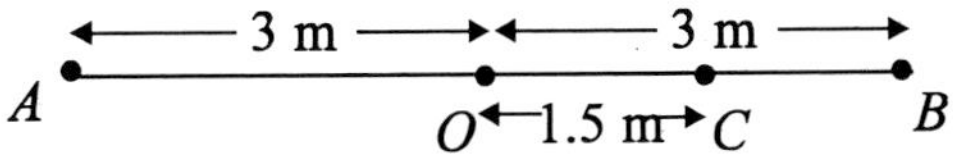

The sketch shows the point C at a distance of 1.5 m from the centre O and the extreme positions A and B of the particle. There are two ways in which the particle can travel twice through the point C in an interval of two seconds

(i) it travels to the right from C to B and then back to C,

(ii) it travels to the left from C to A and then back to C.

(i) The time from O to C can be found by assuming that at $t = 0$ the particle is at O so that its subsequent displacement x m from O is 3 sin ωt. The particle will then pass through C when

$$1.5 = 3 \sin \omega t,$$

the smallest solution of this is $t = \dfrac{\pi}{6\omega}$. The time from O to B is a quarter of the period and therefore the time from C to B and back is $2\left(\dfrac{\pi}{2\omega} - \dfrac{\pi}{6\omega}\right) = \dfrac{2\pi}{3\omega}$, this is given to be 2 seconds so the period, $\dfrac{2\pi}{\omega}$, is 6 seconds.

(ii) The time from C to A and back is twice the sum of the times from C to O and from O to A. The latter time is a quarter of the period and so the total time is

$$2\left(\frac{\pi}{2\omega} + \frac{\pi}{6\omega}\right) = \frac{4\pi}{3\omega}.$$

This is given to be 2 seconds so the period, $\dfrac{2\pi}{\omega}$, is 3 seconds.

Example 3.9

The level of the tide in a certain port is assumed to vary simple harmonically with period 12.4 hours and the difference in level between high and low water is 6 m. On a particular day low water occurs at noon. Find the time when the water level will be increasing at its maximum rate and find this rate in ms^{-1}.

The period is 3600×12.4 s and therefore $\omega = \dfrac{2\pi}{3600 \times 12.4}$.

The amplitude of the oscillation is 3 m, the maximum value of the rate of change occurs at the centre of the oscillation and this occurs a quarter of a period after low water i.e. at time 3.1 hours after noon.

The maximum speed is $a\omega = \dfrac{6\pi}{3600 \times 12.4} = 4.2 \times 10^{-4}$ ms^{-1}.

Example 3.10

A horizontal shelf oscillates vertically with amplitude 0.2 m. Find the least period of oscillations so that a particle placed on the shelf is not jerked off.

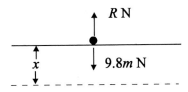

The diagram shows the particle on the shelf and the central position of the shelf. The displacement of the particle above the central position is denoted by x m. If the mass of the particle is m kg then the upward force on the particle is $(R - 9.8m)$ N, where the reaction of the shelf is R N. Newton's law gives

$$m \frac{d^2x}{dt^2} = R - 9.8m.$$

Since the motion is simple harmonic

$$\frac{d^2x}{dt^2} = -\omega^2 x,$$

so that $R = m(9.8 - \omega^2 x)$. The maximum value of x is 0.2 and therefore the reaction will be positive, i.e. the particle will not leave the shelf provided that $9.8 \geq 0.2\omega^2$ i.e. $\omega \leq 7$ and therefore the least period is $\dfrac{2\pi}{7}$ s.

Example 3.11

A horizontal shelf oscillates horizontally with frequency 5 Hz. Find the maximum amplitude so that a particle placed on the shelf does not slide. The coefficient of friction between the shelf and the particle is 0.4.

The diagram shows the particle on the shelf and the central position of the particle is denoted by O and the displacement of the particle from the central position is denoted by x m. The only horizontal force acting on the particle is the friction force F N and if the mass of the particle is m kg then Newton's law gives

$$m \frac{d^2x}{dt^2} = F.$$

The reaction R of the shelf is $9.8m$ N and therefore the maximum magnitude of F without slipping is $0.4R = 3.92m$ N. Therefore the particle will not slip provided that the magnitude of $\dfrac{d^2x}{dt^2}$ is not greater than 3.92 ms^{-2}.

Since the motion is simple harmonic

$$\frac{d^2x}{dt^2} = -\omega^2 x,$$

where $\dfrac{\omega}{2\pi} = 5$ so that $\omega = 10\pi$. The maximum value of $\dfrac{d^2x}{dt^2}$ is therefore $100\pi^2 a$ ms^{-2} where a m denotes the amplitude of the oscillation. Therefore the particle will not slip provided that $a \leq \dfrac{3.92}{100\pi^2} = 3.97 \times 10^{-3}$.

Example 3.12

Find the amplitude, period and centre of the simple harmonic motion defined by $v^2 = 84 - 4x^2 + 16x$.

The general form of the speed for simple harmonic motion is $v^2 = \omega^2(a^2 - (x-b)^2)$, and therefore the first step is to complete the square for the terms involving x and x^2 i.e. $-4x^2 + 16x$. This expression can be rewritten as $-4(x-2)^2 + 16$, so that

$$v^2 = 100 - 4(x-2)^2 = 4(25 - (x-2)^2).$$

Therefore $\omega = 2$, $a^2 = 25$ and $b = 2$ so that the motion is of period π s, amplitude 5 m with centre at the point $x = 2$ m.

Example 3.13

The velocity of a particle describing simple harmonic motion is 4 ms^{-1} at the origin and $\sqrt{13}$ ms^{-1} and 1 ms^{-1} when $x = 1$ m and $x = 3$ m respectively. Find the centre of the motion.

Since the question asks for the centre of the motion it is very unlikely that this will be the origin and therefore the form $v^2 = \omega^2(a^2 - (x-b)^2)$ has to be used.
Substituting the given data in this expression gives

$$16 = \omega^2(a^2 - b^2), \quad 13 = \omega^2(a^2 - (1-b)^2), \quad 1 = \omega^2(a^2 - (3-b)^2).$$

Subtracting the second equation from the first and the third equation from the first gives

$$3 = \omega^2(1 - 2b), \quad 15 = \omega^2(9 - 6b).$$

Dividing these equations to eliminate ω gives $b = -1$, i.e. the centre is at the point where $x = -1$ m.

Exercises 3.1

Questions 1 to 6 refer to a particle P describing simple harmonic motion with centre O; the extreme points of the motion are denoted by A and B.

1   The magnitude of the acceleration is 8 ms^{-2} when $OP = 2$ m. Find the period.

2   The period and greatest speed are $\dfrac{\pi}{5}$ s and 5 ms^{-1}. Find the amplitude of the motion and the length of OP when the speed is 4 ms^{-1}.

3   The greatest acceleration of P is 20 ms^{-2} and it makes 10 oscillations per second. Find its greatest speed.

4   The frequency of the oscillations is 3 Hz and the greatest speed is 10 ms^{-1}. Find the amplitude.

5   The speed of P is 6 ms^{-1} when $OP = 4$ m and 8 ms^{-1} when $OP = 3$ m. Find the amplitude and period of the oscillations.

6   The speed of P is 16 ms^{-1} when $OP = 3$ m and 12 ms^{-1} when $OP = 4$ m. Find the amplitude of the oscillations and the greatest speed of P.

7   The speed of P is 12 ms^{-1} when $BP = 2$ m and 3 ms^{-1} when $BP = 1$ m. Find the amplitude of the motion.

8   The displacement x m of a particle at time t s is given by $x = 4\cos 3t - 2\sin 3t$. Find the amplitude and period of the oscillation.

9   The tip of the needle of a sewing machine travels a distance of 0.025 m from the top to the bottom of its stroke and its maximum speed is 5 ms^{-1}. Assuming the motion is simple harmonic, find its frequency.

10 The blade of a particular jig saw operates at between 1200 and 3000 strokes per minute (a stroke being one movement from top to bottom). The length of the stroke is 0.02 m. Find the range of maximum speeds for the blade.

11 A particle describes simple harmonic motion, centre O, of period 4 s and of amplitude 3m. Find the time taken for the particle to travel from O directly to the point C where $OC = 1$ m and the time taken to travel a further distance of 0.5 m from C.

12 A particle describing simple harmonic motion of amplitude 3 m passes through a point C at intervals of $\dfrac{5\pi}{3}$ s and $\dfrac{7\pi}{3}$ s. Find the distance of C from the centre of the motion.

13 The speed of a particle is 0.4 ms^{-1} at the point A at a distance of 0.06 m from the centre of the oscillation and 0.3 ms^{-1} at the point B, on the same side of O as A with $OB = 0.08$ m. Find the time taken to travel from A to B.

14 The depth of water in a harbour varies simple harmonically about a mean position. On a certain day the depth at high water at 5 a.m. is 10 m and 6 hours 15 minutes later the depth at low water is 5 m. Find the first time after 5 a.m. when the depth of the water is 9 m.

15 On a particular day in a harbour low tide occurs at 10 a.m. and high tide at 4.15 p.m. The depth of the water is 2 m at low water and 5 m at high tide. Assuming that the variation of the water level is simple harmonic find the times between 10 a.m. and 10 p.m. when the depth of the water is greater than 3 m.

16 A body floating in the sea oscillates up and down with the waves with simple harmonic motion. It moves a total vertical distance of 0.4 m and its period is 6 s. Find its greatest speed and greatest acceleration.

17 A horizontal shelf describes vertical oscillations in simple harmonic motion with period 5 s and amplitude 0.5 m. Find the maximum and minimum values of the reaction of the shelf on a particle of mass 0.4 kg resting on it.

18 A horizontal shelf describes vertical oscillations in simple harmonic motion and makes 2 oscillations per second. The amplitude of the oscillations is 0.1 m. Find the height of the shelf above its central position when a small particle on the shelf loses contact with it.

19 A horizontal membrane oscillates vertically in simple harmonic motion with amplitude 0.2 cm. Find the frequency of the oscillation if sand sprinkled on the membrane just loses contact with it.

20 A horizontal platform oscillates horizontally in simple harmonic motion of period $\frac{\pi}{5}$ s and amplitude 0.02 m. Given that the coefficient of friction between the platform and a particle resting on it is 0.25 find whether the particle can stay on the platform without sliding.

21 A horizontal platform oscillates horizontally in simple harmonic motion and makes five complete oscillations per second. The coefficient of friction between the platform and a particle resting on it is 0.1. Find the maximum amplitude of the oscillations so that the particle does not slip on the platform.

22 The speed v ms^{-1} of a particle whose displacement is x m is given by $v^2 = 15 - 5x^2 + 10x$. Find the amplitude, period and centre of the oscillation.

3.3   Dynamical problems

So far it has been given that a motion is simple harmonic but in many real problems the first step is to **establish** that the motion is simple harmonic. Once this has been done the problems effectively become examples of those in the previous section.

The basic method for establishing S.H.M., as for all dynamical problems, is to pick a reference direction and work out the forces in that direction and then set mass × acceleration = force.

If the motion is simple harmonic then you will end up with one of the equations

$$\frac{d^2x}{dt^2} = -\omega^2 x,$$

$$\frac{d^2x}{dt^2} = -\omega^2 (x - b).$$

The second equation corresponds to the centre being at $x = b$.

If in an examination paper you see one of the above equations **you know that you have a problem on S.H.M**. Most problems on particles moving at the end of elastic springs and strings involve simple harmonic motion and if you come across such a problem then, once again, you know that you are extremely likely to be dealing with simple harmonic motion.

You have already come across problems involving elastic springs and strings where you used energy conservation. This gave that the speed v was given by an expression of the form $v^2 = px^2 + qx + r$, which is effectively of the form $\omega^2(a^2 - (x - b)^2)$ as was shown in Example 3.12. This is the general form for S.H.M. centre $x = b$, so you could compare coefficients to find a, b and ω. If all you have to find are speeds and displacements then the energy method is an equivalent alternative but, if you need times from point to point, then you need to use expressions of the form $x = a\sin(\omega t + \varepsilon)$ or $x = A\cos\omega t + B\sin\omega t$.

There is a very important difference between strings and springs which you have to be very careful about. Springs exert forces when both extended and compressed, whereas strings only exert forces when extended. As you will see in the following examples the effect of this is that a particle at the end of an elastic string only describes simple harmonic motion when the string is extended.

Example 3.14

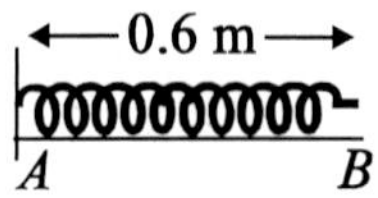

The diagram shows a spring of natural length 0.6 m and modulus 0.48 N on a smooth horizontal table. One end of the spring is fixed to a point A on the table and the spring initially lies at rest, and of length 0.6 m, with its free end at the point B of the table. A particle P of mass 0.2 kg is then attached to the free end and at time $t = 0$ the spring is extended a distance of 0.06 m and released from rest. Show that at a subsequent time t s   the displacement x m of P from B, in the sense from A to B, satisfies the differential equation

$$\frac{d^2x}{dt^2} = -4x.$$

Write down an expression for x at time t s and find the time that elapses until

(i) the extension of the spring is first 0.02 m,

(ii) the distance of P from O is 0.58 m.

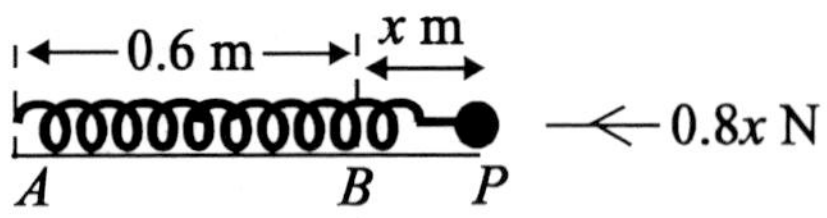

The reference direction is given to be in the sense from A to B and therefore when the extension is x m the tension in the spring is of magnitude $\dfrac{0.48x}{0.6}$ N $= 0.8x$ N and acts from B to A and therefore the force in the positive x direction is $-0.8\,x$ N.

If x is negative then the spring is compressed a distance of $-x$ m and it exerts a force in the positive x direction of $-\dfrac{0.48x}{0.6}$ N $= -0.8x$ N, therefore the force in the positive x direction is $-0.8x$ N. In practice you would not normally be expected to analyse the force as carefully as this and, unless told to the contrary, it is safe to assume that when the displacement of a particle, at the end of a spring, in a given sense is x then the force in the same sense is $-\dfrac{\lambda x}{l}$. In this expression λ denotes the modulus and l the natural length.

Applying Newton's law gives

$$0.2\,\frac{d^2x}{dt^2} = -0.8x,$$

i.e.
$$\frac{d^2x}{dt^2} = -4x.$$

This equation immediately tells you that the motion is simple harmonic with centre B and with $\omega = 2$. The particle is released from a point of rest i.e. from an extreme point so the amplitude is the initial distance of P from O i.e. 0.06 m and since $x = 0.06$ at $t = 0$ the subsequent displacement from O is given by $x = 0.06 \cos 2t$.

(i) Therefore $x = 0.02$ when

$$0.02 = 0.06 \cos 2t,$$

and this first occurs when $2t = \cos^{-1} \dfrac{1}{3}$ so that $t = 0.62$.

(ii) In this case $x = -0.02$ i.e. t satisfies

$$-0.02 = 0.06 \cos 2t,$$

so that

$$t = \frac{1}{2} \cos^{-1} \left(-\frac{1}{3} \right) = 0.96.$$

Example 3.15

Answer parts (i) and (ii) of the previous example when the particle P is projected at time $t=0$ from B with a speed of 0.08 ms^{-1} in the sense from A to B.

The only difference in this case is that the particle is at the centre at time $t = 0$ so that the displacement is given by $x = \pm a \sin 2t$. Since the velocity is in the direction of x increasing the positive sign has to be chosen. The maximum speed occurs at the centre i.e. at B and is $a\omega = 2a$ so that $a = 0.04$. Therefore $x = 0.04 \sin 2t$ and the extension of the spring is 0.02 m when

$$0.02 = 0.04 \sin 2t,$$

and this first occurs when $2t = \sin^{-1} \dfrac{1}{2}$ so that $t = \dfrac{\pi}{12}$.

Similarly for $x = -0.02$

$$-0.02 = 0.04 \sin 2t,$$

and this first occurs when $2t = \sin^{-1} \left(-\dfrac{1}{2} \right)$ so that $t = \dfrac{7\pi}{12}$.

Example 3.16

Answer parts (i) and (ii) of Example 3.14 when the spring is replaced by a string of the same modulus and natural length.

In this case the main difference is in the equation of motion which only holds for x positive. For x negative the string is slack and P moves with zero acceleration i.e. at constant speed.

The time to reach the extension of 0.02 is still the same.

However after P has passed through B it will move with a constant speed, this is the speed at B i.e. $a\omega = 0.12$ ms^{-1} so that $x = -0.02$ at a time $\dfrac{0.02}{0.12}$ s $= 0.17$ s after passing through B.

The time taken to reach B is a quarter of the period i.e. $\dfrac{\pi}{2\omega} = \dfrac{\pi}{4}$s $= 0.79$ s.

Therefore $t = 0.17 + 0.79 = 0.96$.

Example 3.17

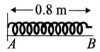

The diagram shows a spring of natural length 0.8 m and modulus 6 N on a smooth horizontal table. One end of the spring is fixed to a point A on the table and a particle P of mass 0.3 kg is attached to the free end. The particle is set in motion and at time $t = 0$ the extension of the spring is 0.1 m and the particle is moving with speed 0.3 ms^{-1} towards the point A. Find the extension of the spring at time t s and also the amplitude of the oscillations.

Since the extension is required as a function of time then the most appropriate method of solution is to find the equation of motion.

The equilibrium position is taken to be at the point B and when the extension is x m (with $x > 0$) the tension in the spring is of magnitude $\dfrac{6x}{0.8}$ N $= 7.5x$ N and acts in the sense from B to A and therefore the force in the positive x direction is $-7.5x$ N.

This will also be the force in the positive x direction for x negative and therefore applying Newton's law gives

$$0.3\,\dfrac{d^2x}{dt^2} = -7.5x,$$

i.e.

$$\dfrac{d^2x}{dt^2} = -25x.$$

This equation immediately tells you that the motion is simple harmonic about B with $\omega = 5$.

In this case, since conditions are not given at time $t = 0$ at either the centre or an extreme point, the general solution $x = A \cos 5t + B \sin 5t$ has to be used. For $t = 0$, $x = 0.1$ and $\frac{dx}{dt} = -0.3$ (the particle is moving towards A). Therefore $A = 0.1$ and

$5B = -0.3$ so that $B = -0.06$ so that

$$x = 0.1 \cos 5t - 0.06 \sin 5t.$$

To find the amplitude this expression has to be written in the form

$$x = a \sin(5t + \varepsilon) = a \sin 5t \cos \varepsilon + a \cos 5t \sin \varepsilon.$$

Therefore $-0.06 = a \cos \varepsilon$ and $0.1 = a \sin \varepsilon$. Squaring and adding these gives

$$a = \sqrt{0.06^2 + 0.1^2} = 0.12,$$

so that the amplitude is 0.12 m.

It is worth looking also at the alternative method using energy conservation.

When the extension is x m the elastic energy in the spring is $\frac{1}{2} \times \frac{6x^2}{0.8}$ J $= 3.75x^2$ J,

and therefore, if v ms^{-1} denotes the speed of the particle, energy conservation gives

$$\frac{1}{2} \times 0.3v^2 + 3.75x^2 = \text{constant.}$$

The constant can be found from substituting the initial values of x and v so that

$$0.15v^2 + 3.75x^2 = 0.15 \times 0.3^2 + 3.75 \times 0.1^2,$$

this equation can be rearranged into the standard form for S.H. M. as

$$v^2 = -25x^2 + 0.3^2 + 25 \times 0.1^2,$$

or

$$v^2 = 25\left(\frac{0.3^2 + 25 \times 0.1^2 - x^2}{25}\right) = 25(0.06^2 + 0.1^2 - x^2).$$

Therefore the motion is simple harmonic with $\omega = 5$ and amplitude $\sqrt{0.06^2 + 0.1^2}$. Once you have shown the motion is simple harmonic and found ω you can quote the general solution and solve the problem as above. The differential equation for x can be found by differentiating the expression for v^2 with respect to x and using $v\frac{dv}{dx} = \frac{d^2x}{dt^2}$.

Example 3.18

A particle P of mass 0.1 kg is attached to one end of an elastic spring, the other end A of which is held fixed and the particle can move in a vertical line through A. The spring is of natural length 1 m and modulus 4.9 N. Find the depth below A of the point B where the particle can rest in equilibrium. The spring is then further extended until P is a distance of 0.1 m below B and then released from rest. Show that the motion is simple harmonic with centre B and find the time taken until P first reaches B.

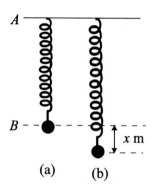

(a)   (b)

Diagram (a) shows the equilibrium position with the equilibrium extension being denoted by d m. The forces acting on the particle are 0.1 x 9.8 N downwards and the tension $4.9d$ N acting upward. For equilibrium these are equal i.e. $0.98 = 4.9d$ so that $d = 0.2$ and therefore the point B is at a depth of 1.2 m below A.

It is required to show that the motion is simple harmonic with centre B and therefore its seems reasonable to use the downward displacement x m of P from B as a variable, as shown in diagram (b). The force in the downward direction due to the tension in the string is therefore $-4.9(0.2 + x)$ N, the force in this direction due to gravity is 0.98 N so that the total force in the direction of increasing x is

$$- 4.9(0.2 + x)\, \text{N} + 0.98\, \text{N} = - 4.9x\, \text{N}.$$

Applying Newton's law gives, that at time t s,

$$0.1\, \frac{\mathrm{d}^2 x}{\mathrm{d}t^2} = - 4.9x,$$

or

$$\frac{\mathrm{d}^2 x}{\mathrm{d}t^2} = - 49\, x,$$

the motion is therefore simple harmonic with $\omega^2 = 49$ and the centre of the oscillation is at B. The time for P to first reach B is a quarter of a period i.e. $\dfrac{\pi}{14}$ s.

For any motion at the end of a spring it turns out that the motion is always simple harmonic about the equilibrium position and it therefore pays (it avoids algebra) to measure the displacement from this point

Example 3.19

An elastic string of natural length 0.5 m, one end of which is fixed at a point A, is extended a distance of 0.1 m by a particle P hanging freely from its other end. The particle is then pulled down a further distance of d m and released from rest. Find the time taken by the particle to reach its maximum height when
(a) $d = 0.05$, (b) $d = 0.15$.

This question is fairly similar to the previous one except that neither the mass of the particle nor the modulus of the string are given, these are denoted by m kg and λ N respectively. In equilibrium the forces acting on the particle are 9.8 m N downwards and the tension $\dfrac{0.1\lambda}{0.5}$ N $=$ 0.2λ N acting upward. For equilibrium these are equal i.e. $\lambda = 49m$.

As stated above it is a good idea to measure displacement from the equilibrium position and x m denotes the downward displacement of P from the equilibrium point B as shown in the diagram.

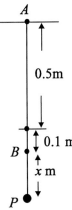

The force in the downward direction due to the tension in the string is therefore $\dfrac{-\lambda(0.1+x)}{0.5}$ N $= -2\lambda(0.1+x)$ the force in this direction due to gravity is 9.8m N so that the total force in the direction of increasing x is $-2\lambda(0.1+x)$ N $+$ 9.8m N $= -2\lambda x$ N , since $\lambda = 49m$. Applying Newton's law gives, that at time t s,

$$m\frac{\mathrm{d}^2 x}{\mathrm{d}t^2} = -2\lambda x$$

or

$$\frac{\mathrm{d}^2 x}{\mathrm{d}t^2} = -98x.$$

The motion appears to be simple harmonic with $\omega^2 = 98$ and the centre of the oscillation is at B. There is a slight problem in that the equation of motion has been obtained assuming that the string is never slack and the possibility of being slack has to be considered.

Case (a) For simple harmonic motion with the particle released from a point 0.05 m below the centre the maximum height above B would be at the other extreme point i.e. at a height of 0.05 m above B. At this point the string is not yet slack and therefore the equation of S.H.M. is still valid and the time to the point of maximum height is half a period i.e. $\dfrac{\pi}{\sqrt{98}}$.

Case (b) Assuming simple harmonic motion gives the maximum height above B to be 0.15 m, however the string would have become slack at a height of 0.1 m above B and therefore the equations of S.H.M. no longer hold. In this case once the particle has reached the point where the string is no longer taut (i.e at a height of 0.1 m above B) the particle moves under the action of gravity alone. Therefore to find the time that it is in motion it is necessary to find the velocity when $x = -0.1$ m. Up to reaching this point the motion will have been simple harmonic with amplitude 0.15 m so that, at time t s, $x = 0.15 \cos\sqrt{98}\, t$, where $t = 0$ is the time of release and $v^2 = 98\,(0.15^2 - x^2)$. Substituting $x = -0.1$ gives the speed with which the particle starts moving under gravity alone as 1.11 ms^{-1} and the time to reach the highest point is $\dfrac{1.11}{9.8}$ s $= 0.11$ s. The time taken to reach the point $x = -0.1$ is found by solving

$$-0.1 = 0.15 \cos\sqrt{98}\, t,$$

the solution is $t = 0.23$. The total time taken from rest to reach the highest point is $(0.11 + 0.23)$ s $= 0.34$ s.

Example 3.20

P

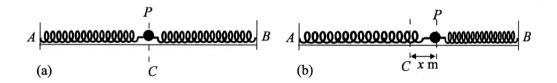

The diagram shows a particle P of mass 0.2 kg lying on a smooth horizontal table and attached by two springs of natural lengths 0.6 m and 0.4 m and moduli 3 N and 6 N respectively, to points A and B where $AB = 1.4$ m. Find the distance from A of the point C where the particle is in equilibrium. Show that if the particle is disturbed from C then it will describe simple harmonic motion about C and find the period of this motion.

(a)   (b)

The equilibrium position is shown in diagram (a) above, and the distance AC is denoted by d m. The extension of the spring attached to A is $(d - 0.6)$ m and the extension of the other spring $(1 - d)$ m. The tensions in the springs are therefore $\dfrac{3(d - 0.6)}{0.6}$ N and $\dfrac{6(1 - d)}{0.4}$ N.

In equilibrium these are equal, i.e. $\dfrac{3(d - 0.6)}{0.6} = \dfrac{6(1 - d)}{0.4}$ giving $d = 0.9$.

When the particle is set in motion its subsequent displacement from C in the sense from A to B is denoted by x m as shown in diagram (b). The extension of the spring attached to A is $(d + x - 0.6)$ m and therefore the force acting on P due to this spring is $-\dfrac{3(d + x - 0.6)}{0.6}$N in the positive x direction. The extension of the spring attached to B is $(1 - d - x)$ m and therefore the force acting on P due to this string is $\dfrac{6(1 - d - x)}{0.4}$ N in the positive x direction. The total force in the positive x direction is therefore

$$-\frac{3(d + x - 0.6)}{0.6} \text{N} + \frac{6(1 - d - x)}{0.4}\text{N},$$

and on using the value for d, this simplifies to $- 20x$N. Newton's law gives

$$0.2\,\frac{d^2 x}{dt^2} = - 20x,$$

i.e

$$\frac{d^2 x}{dt^2} = -100x.$$

The motion is therefore simple harmonic with period $\dfrac{2\pi}{10}$ s $= \dfrac{\pi}{5}$s.

Exercises 3.2

In questions 1 to 3 a spring of modulus λ N, natural length a m is placed on a smooth horizontal plane. One end of the spring is fixed at a point A, a particle P of mass m kg is attached to the other end and the particle is free to move in the line of the spring.

1    $m = 0.1$, $\lambda = 10$, $a = 1$, the spring is extended a distance of 0.2 m and P released from rest. Find the time taken

(a) until the extension is first equal to 0.05 m,

(b) until AP is first equal to 0.97 m.

2    $m = 0.8$, $\lambda = 2.56$, $a = 0.8$, at time $t = 0$ the particle is projected from its equilibrium position with speed 0.8 ms^{-1} directly towards A. Find expressions for the displacement and velocity of the particle at a subsequent time t s.

3    $m = 1.5$, $\lambda = 27$, $a = 2$, the particle is projected from its equilibrium position in the sense directly away from A with speed 1.2 ms^{-1}. Find the time that elapses before $AP = 1.9$ m.

4   Answer question 1 when the spring is replaced by a string of the same modulus and natural length.

5   Answer question 3 when the spring is replaced by a string of the same modulus and natural length.

In questions 6 and 7 a particle P of mass m kg is suspended from one end of a spring of modulus λ N, natural length a m, the other end of the spring being fixed at A. The particle is free to move along the vertical through A.

6 $m = 0.5$, $\lambda = 16$, $a = 0.5$, the particle is initially at rest in the equilibrium position and then pulled down a further distance of 0.04 m and released from rest. Find the time taken for the particle to

(a) first return to the equilibrium position,

(b) to first attain a height of 0.01 m above the equilibrium position.

7 $m = 1.5$, $\lambda = 30$, $a = 0.8$, the particle is initially at rest at its equilibrium position and it is then projected vertically downwards with a speed of 1 ms^{-1}. Find the maximum depth of the particle below its equilibrium position and the time taken to drop a distance of 0.05m from the equilibrium position.

8   A particle P of mass 0.1 kg is attached to one end of an elastic string, the other end A of which is held fixed and the particle can move in a vertical line through A. The string is of natural length 1 m and modulus 4.9 N. The particle is initially at rest when it is pulled down a distance of 0.4 m below its equilibrium position and released. Find the time taken between the string becoming slack and the particle reaching its highest point.

9   A particle P of mass 0.1 kg is suspended in equilibrium from a spring and the extension of the spring is 0.1 m. When P is in equilibrium an additional mass of 0.2 kg is gently attached to it and the combined particle released. Find the period and amplitude of the subsequent simple harmonic motion.

10   One end of a spring is held fixed and two particles of mass 0.4 kg and m kg are attached together to the other end and hang in equilibrium. When they are displaced a small distance below the equilibrium point and released they make simple harmonic oscillations of period 0.5 s. If the particle of mass 0.4 kg is removed the other particle, when displaced from its equilibrium position, makes simple harmonic oscillations of period 0.25 s. Find m.

11   Two points A and B lie on a horizontal line at a distance of 3 m apart. A particle P, in the region between A and B, of mass 0.6 kg is attached by one of two identical strings of modulus 20 N and natural length 1 m to A and to B. The particle is displaced a distance of 0.1 m from its equilibrium position along the line AB and released from rest. Show that its subsequent motion is simple harmonic and find its period.

12   A particle lying on a smooth horizontal table is attached by a spring of natural length 0.6 m to a fixed point on the table. The spring is held at the point A where the extension of the string is 0.1 m and then released from rest. It first returns to A after $\dfrac{\pi}{2}$ s. Find the speed of the particle when it is at a distance of 0.02 m from A and the time taken to reach this point.

13 When a particle of mass 5 kg is suspended from a spring the extension is 0.2 m. Find the maximum speed of the particle when it is pulled down a further distance of 0.2 m and released from rest.

3.4   Damped harmonic motion

In the problems in the previous section it was shown that a particle moving at the end of a spring would describe simple harmonic motion, which is a periodic motion which can go on indefinitely. Such a motion of course cannot exist in reality and, if you observed the motion of a particle at the end of a spring, you would see that the oscillations gradually die down. This is due to the effect of air or frictional resistance and the simple model has to be refined to take this resistance into account.

There are, as discussed in section 2.3, many possible models of resistance but the only one which leads to reasonably easy mathematics when refining problems involving springs is that which assumes that the resistance is directly proportional to the speed. Apart from resistance ocurring naturally there are many instances where damping is introduced to avoid oscillations continuing. For example a simple model of the suspension of a car would be a particle on top of a spring and therefore in this model the car would move up and down and be uncomfortable to drive in. In order to avoid this a damping system is introduced, this consists of a system of dashpots and these are constructed so that they exert a resistance proportional to speed. A dashpot is effectively a cylinder containing fluid with a closely fitting piston, which may have a small hole in it, when the piston is moved then the fluid seeps through the edges and through the hole and the resistance to the motion is approximately proportional to the speed of the piston. In modelling oscillations of a vibrating mass the mass is assumed to be connected to the dashpot as shown in the diagram.

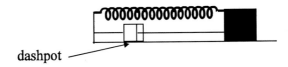

dashpot

The shock absorbers of a car are effectively dashpots.

Therefore the model assuming resistance proportional to speed is a particularly useful one because it is a reasonable model of many systems where damping has to be introduced for practical reasons.

Example 3.21

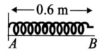

The diagram shows a spring of natural length 0.6 m and modulus 0.48 N on a smooth horizontal table. One end of the spring is fixed to a point A on the table and the spring initially lies at rest, and of length 0.6 m, with its free end at the point B of the table. A particle P of mass 0.2 kg is then attached to the free end and at time $t = 0$ the spring is extended a distance of 0.06 m and released from rest. There is a resistance to the motion of magnitude $0.4v$ N when the particle is moving with speed v ms^{-1}. Show that at a subsequent time t s the displacement x m of P from B, in the sense from A to B, satisfies the differential equation

$$\frac{d^2x}{dt^2} + 2\frac{dx}{dt} + 4x = 0.$$

Obtain an expression for x at time t s and discuss the subsequent motion.

(This is example 3.14 with an additional resistance term included.)

The reference direction is given to be in the sense from A to B and therefore when the displacement from B is x m it follows as in the previous examples that the force in the positive x direction is $-\dfrac{0.48x}{0.6} = -0.8x$ N.

When the particle is moving to the right its speed is $\dfrac{dx}{dt}$ ms^{-1} and therefore the resistive force acting on it is to the left and of magnitude $0.4\dfrac{dx}{dt}$ N, so that the force due to the resistance is $-0.4\dfrac{dx}{dt}$ N in the positive x direction.

When the particle is moving to the left its speed is $-\dfrac{dx}{dt}$ ms^{-1}, as $\dfrac{dx}{dt}$ is now negative, and therefore the resistive force acting on it is to the right and of magnitude $-0.4\dfrac{dx}{dt}$ N, so that the force due to the resistance is $-0.4\dfrac{dx}{dt}$ N in the positive x direction. Therefore whichever direction the particle is moving in the force in the positive x direction is $-0.4\dfrac{dx}{dt}$ N. You would not normally be expected to analyse the situation as carefully and can usually assume that if the resistance is cv N then the force in the positive x direction is $-c\dfrac{dx}{dt}$ N. It is not always true, whatever the resistance law, that the force in the reference direction is the same whatever the direction of motion. (The result can be shown to be true whenever the resistance is an odd function of speed)

Applying Newton's law gives

$$0.2\,\frac{d^2x}{dt^2} = -0.8x - 0.4\frac{dx}{dt},$$

i.e.
$$\frac{d^2x}{dt^2} + 2\frac{dx}{dt} + 4x = 0.$$

This is a second order equation with constant coefficients and trying, as shown in Chapter 1, the substitution $x = e^{mt}$ gives the auxiliary equation

$$m^2 + 2m + 4 = 0.$$

The roots of this are $-1 \pm \sqrt{-3}$. It now follows from part (c) of the summary in section 1.2 that the general solution is

$$x = e^{-t}(A\cos\sqrt{3}\,t + B\sin\sqrt{3}\,t).$$

Differentiating this with respect to t gives

$$\frac{dx}{dt} = -e^{-t}(A\cos\sqrt{3}\,t + B\sin\sqrt{3t}) + \sqrt{3}\,e^{-t}(-A\sin\sqrt{3}\,t + B\cos\sqrt{3}\,t).$$

Initially $x = 0.06$ and $\dfrac{dx}{dt} = 0$, and therefore substituting $t = 0$ into the above expressions gives, $A = 0.06$ and $\sqrt{3}\,B = A$ so that

$$x = 0.06\,e^{-t}\left(\cos\sqrt{3}t + \frac{1}{\sqrt{3}}\sin\sqrt{3}t\right).$$

The general form of the motion is seen most easily by rewriting the part in brackets in the form $a\sin(\sqrt{3}t + \varepsilon)$ where

$$a\cos\varepsilon = \frac{1}{\sqrt{3}} \quad\text{and}\quad a\sin\varepsilon = 1.$$

Squaring and adding gives $a = \dfrac{2}{\sqrt{3}}$ so that $\varepsilon = \dfrac{\pi}{3}$ and

$$x = \frac{0.12}{\sqrt{3}}\,e^{-t}\sin\left(\sqrt{3}t + \frac{\pi}{3}\right).$$

x will be zero for $t = \dfrac{1}{\sqrt{3}}\left(-\dfrac{\pi}{3}\right),\ \dfrac{1}{\sqrt{3}}\left(\dfrac{5\pi}{3}\right)$ .... i.e at intervals $\dfrac{\pi}{\sqrt{3}}$.

Also $\dfrac{dx}{dt}$ will vanish when

$$\sin\left(\sqrt{3}t + \frac{\pi}{3}\right) = \sqrt{3}\cos\left(\sqrt{3}t + \frac{\pi}{3}\right)$$

i.e. $t = 0, \dfrac{\pi}{\sqrt{3}}, \dots\dots$ i.e. at intervals $\dfrac{\pi}{\sqrt{3}}$.

The general form will therefore be as in the following diagram, there will be an oscillation in the sense that P will keep on returning to B but the distances from B of the points of zero velocity will keep on decreasing and x tends to zero exponentially so that the motion will gradually cease. The motion will lie between the two curves $x = \pm \dfrac{0.12}{\sqrt{3}} e^{-t}$ as shown below.

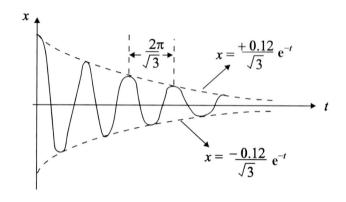

In this kind of motion, where some kind of oscillation exists, the damping is said to be weak or sub-critical.

Example 3.22

We now consider the previous problem when the resistive force is $0.8\,v$ N.

The difference in this case is that the force in the positive x direction is now $-0.8\dfrac{dx}{dt}$ N and applying Newton's law gives

$$0.2\,\frac{d^2x}{dt^2} = -0.8\,x - 0.8\,\frac{dx}{dt},$$

i.e.

$$\frac{d^2x}{dt^2} + 4\frac{dx}{dt} + 4x = 0.$$

This is a second order equation with constant coefficients and trying, as shown in Chapter 1, the substitution $x = e^{mt}$ gives the auxiliary equation

$$m^2 + 4m + 4 = 0.$$

There is only one root of this i.e. $m = -2$ and it now follows from part (b) of the summary in section 1.5 that the general solution is

$$x = e^{-2t}(At + B).$$

Initially $x = 0.06$ and $\dfrac{dx}{dt} = 0$ so that $B = 0.06$ and $A = 2B = 0.12$.

The general solution is therefore
$$x = e^{-2t}(0.12t + 0.06).$$
Differentiating this expression gives $\dfrac{dx}{dt} = -0.24t\,e^{-2t}$.

Therefore x does not vanish for positive t and the form of x will be as shown below.

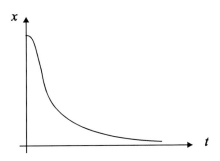

The damping in this case is said to be critical.

Example 3.23

We now consider the previous problem when the resistive force is v N.

In this case the force in the positive x direction is now $-\dfrac{dx}{dt}$ N and applying Newton's law gives
$$0.2\,\frac{d^2x}{dt^2} = -0.8\,x - \frac{dx}{dt},$$
i.e.
$$\frac{d^2x}{dt^2} + 5\frac{dx}{dt} + 4x = 0.$$

This is a second order equation with constant coefficients and trying, as shown in Chapter 1, the substitution $x = e^{mt}$ gives the auxiliary equation
$$m^2 + 5m + 4 = 0.$$
The roots of this are $m = -1$ and $m = -4$ and it now follows from part (a) of the summary in 1.2 that the general solution is
$$x = Ae^{-t} + Be^{-4t}.$$
Initially $x = 0.06$ and $\dfrac{dx}{dt} = 0$ so that $A + B = 0.06$ and $A + 4B = 0$, so that $B = -0.02$ and $A = 0.08$ and the general solution is therefore
$$x = 0.08e^{-t} - 0.02e^{-4t}.$$
For x to be zero $e^{3t} = 0.25$ and this does not occur for positive t. Therefore the general form for x will be as shown below and again it decreases exponentially with time.

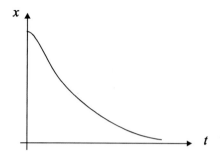

In this case the damping is said to be strong or overcritical.

Exercises 3.3

In questions 1 to 4 a spring of modulus λ N and natural length a m is placed on a smooth horizontal plane. One end of the spring is fixed at a point A, a particle P of mass m kg is attached to the other and the particle is free to move in the line of the spring though the particle, when moving with speed v ms^{-1}, is subject to a resistance to its motion of magnitude kv N.

1    $m = 0.4$, $\lambda = 31.2$, $a = 0.5$, $k = 10$. The particle is displaced a distance of 0.04 m from its equilibrium position in the direction away from A and released from rest. Find its displacement from the equilibrium position at any subsequent time.

2    $m = 0.5$, $\lambda = 48$, $a = 0.6$, $k = 4$. The particle is projected from the equilibrium position in the direction away from A with speed 0.6 ms^{-1}. Find its displacement from the equilibrium position at any subsequent time.

3    $m = 0.8$, $\lambda = 12$, $a = 0.75$, $k = 7.2$. The particle is displaced a distance of 0.2 m from its equilibrium position in the direction towards A and released from rest. Find its displacement from the equilibrium position at any subsequent time.

4    $m = 0.6$, $\lambda = 12$, $a = 0.8$, $k = 6$. The particle is projected from the equilibrium position with speed 0.2 ms^{-1} in the direction towards A. Find its displacement from the equilibrium position at any subsequent time.

5   A simple model of the motion of a particle at the end of a spring shows that it describes simple harmonic motion of period $\dfrac{2\pi}{5}$ s. Find the time between succcessive maxima of its motion when the resistance per unit mass to its motion, when moving with speed v ms^{-1}, is assumed to be $8v$ N.

6   A particle, when resistive forces are ignored, makes simple harmonic oscillations of period $\dfrac{2\pi}{\omega}$ s. Show that if the resistance to the motion is assumed to be $2kv$ N per unit mass when the particle is moving with speed v ms^{-1} then the time between successive maxima is $\dfrac{2\pi}{\sqrt{\omega^2 - k^2}}$ s.

7 A particle which is predicted to describe simple harmonic motion of period 8 s in the absence of resistance is actually observed to attain its successive maximum points from its equilibrium position at intervals of 10 s. Assuming this to be due to a resistance to the motion of $2kv$ N per unit mass when the particle is moving with speed v ms^{-1} find k.

8 The time between successive maxima of the displacement of a particle describing damped harmonic motion is 0.1 s. The ratio of the displacements at successive maxima is 0.9. Given that the particle is of mass 0.4 kg find the resistance to its motion when moving with speed 3 ms^{-1}.

Miscellaneous Exercises 3

1 A particle P moving along the x axis describes simple harmonic motion with the origin as centre so that its displacement from O at time t satisfies the equation
$$\frac{d^2x}{dt^2} + \omega^2 x = 0.$$
Given that P is instantaneously at rest when $x = a$, show from the above equation that v, the speed of the particle at time t, satisfies
$$v^2 = \omega^2(a^2 - x^2).$$
Given that the particle is at O when $t = 0$, prove that
$$x = a \sin \omega t.$$
Given that the period of the motion is $\dfrac{2\pi}{3}$ seconds and that its maximum speed is 24ms^{-1}, find

(i) the amplitude of the motion,

(ii) the time taken for P to travel from O directly to a point 4 m from O.

Given that the particle is of mass 0.25 kg, find

(iii) the rate at which the force acting on P is working when $t = \dfrac{\pi}{9}$ s,

(iv) the maximum rate of working of this force.

2 A particle moves along the x - axis and describes simple harmonic motion about the origin O with period 6 seconds. When $t = 0$ s, $x = 1$ m and the particle is approaching O with speed $\dfrac{\pi}{\sqrt{3}}$ ms^{-1}. Given that the displacement is of the form $x = a \sin(\omega t + \varepsilon)$ find, ω, a, ε and the maximum speed of the particle.

3 Find the general solution of the differential equation

$$\frac{d^2x}{dt^2} + 2\frac{dx}{dt} + 5x = 0.$$

A particle of mass 0.25 kg moves along the x - axis and at time t s its displacement from O in the positive x direction is x m. The force acting on the particle in the positive x direction is $\left(ax + b\frac{dx}{dt}\right)$ N, where a and b are constants. When $x = 2$ and the particle is moving away from the origin with speed 3 ms^{-1} the force acting on it is 4 N in the negative x direction. When, at the same point, the particle is moving towards O with speed 3 ms^{-1} the force acting on it is 1 N in the negative x direction. Show that $a = -\frac{5}{4}$ and find the numerical value of b.

Hence show that x satisfies the above differential equation. At time $t = 0$ the particle is projected towards O from the point $x = 2$ with speed 2 ms^{-1}. Find x in terms of t.

Give a sketch showing how x varies with t.

4 One end of a light elastic string of modulus 4.9 N and natural length 0.5 m is attached to a fixed point A and a particle of mass 0.1 kg is attached to the other end.

The particle is held at A and released from rest. Its speed after it has dropped a distance of x m is v ms^{-1}.

(i) Write down an expression for the speed of the particle when $x \leq 0.5$.

(ii) Show, by use of energy or otherwise, that for $x \geq 0.5$,

$$v^2 = 117.6x - 98x^2 - 24.5.$$

(iii) Show that the acceleration of the particle, for $x \geq 0.5$, is $98(0.6 - x)$.

Deduce that, for $x \geq 0.5$, the motion is simple harmonic. Find the position of the centre of simple harmonic motion and the time taken from the centre to the lowest point reached.

(iv) Find the maximum speed and the maximum depth reached below A.

5 A particle P moves horizontally along the x-axis and describes simple harmonic motion with centre O. At a particular instant $x = 0.04$ m and the magnitudes of the velocity and acceleration of P are 0.2 ms^{-1} and 1 ms^{-2} respectively. Find

(i) the period of the motion,

(ii) the amplitude of the motion.

At time $t = 0$ s the particle is passing through O in the direction of increasing x.
Find

(iii) x at any subsequent time,

(iv) the least positive value of t (correct to two decimal places) when $x = 0.4$ m.

The simple harmonic motion is produced by a light elastic spring, one end of which is attached to P and the other end to the point $x = -0.5$ m. Given that the mass of P is 0.3kg, find the elastic modulus of the spring.

6   A particle P moving along the x-axis describes simple harmonic motion of period $\dfrac{2\pi}{\omega}$ and amplitude a with the origin O as centre. Given that P is at $x = a$ at time $t = 0$, write down an expression in terms of a, ω and t for the displacement x of P from O at any subsequent time t.

Find, in terms of ω, the time taken for P to travel

(i) from the point $x = a$ directly to the point $x = \dfrac{a}{2}$,

(ii) from the point $x = \dfrac{a}{2}$ directly to the point $x = -\dfrac{a}{\sqrt{2}}$.

The speed of P at the point A, where $x = x_1$, is $4b\omega$. The speed of P at the point B, where $x = x_2$, $(x_2 > x_1)$ is $3b\omega$. Given that $AB = 7b$

(iii) show that $x_1 + x_2 = b$ and hence find x_2 in terms of b,

(iv) determine a in terms of b.

7   A horizontal shelf moves vertically in simple harmonic motion and makes 10 complete oscillations in time 4π s. The maximum speed of the shelf is 1 ms^{-1}. Find the amplitude of the motion.

Given that there is a small particle of mass 0.2 kg on the shelf, find the maximum value of the reaction of the shelf on the particle.

8   Find the solution of the differential equation

$$\frac{d^2 x}{dt^2} + 2\frac{dx}{dt} + 50x = 0$$

with $x = 0.28$ and $\dfrac{dx}{dt} = 0$ when $t = 0$.

A particle P of mass 0.2 kg is attached to one end of an elastic spring of modulus of elasticity 10 N and natural length 1m. The other end of the spring is attached to a fixed point A on a horizontal plane. The particle is free to move in a horizontal line through A but its motion is resisted by a force acting in the opposite direction to its motion and when the speed of P is v ms^{-1} the force acting is $0.4v$ N. At time $t = 0$ the particle is moved so that the spring is straight and extended a distance of 0.28 m, the particle is then released from rest. Show that the extension x m of the spring satisfies the above differential equation. Find the minimum length of the spring in the subsequent motion.

9   A particle P of mass 0.1 kg is attached to one end of a light elastic spring of natural length 0.5 m. The other end of the spring is attached to a fixed point O. The particle is hanging freely in equilibrium at the point B where $OB = 0.598$ m.
(i)   Find the elastic modulus of the spring.
At time $t = 0$ the particle is pulled down to a point 0.1 m vertically below B and then released from rest. The subsequent displacement of P from B at time t is denoted by x m and air resistance is to be neglected.
(ii)   Express, in terms of x, the force exerted by the spring.
(iii) Show that
$$\frac{d^2x}{dt^2} + 100x = 0.$$
(iv) Find the time when P is next at a distance of 0.1 m below B.
(v)   Find the speed of P when at a distance of 0.05 m below B.
(vi) Without further calculation explain why the answer to (iv) would be different if the spring were replaced by a string of the same modulus.

10   A particle of mass 0.2 kg moves in a straight line with simple harmonic motion of amplitude 0.6 m and period 6 s. At time t s after leaving O, the centre of the oscillation, the displacement of the particle from O is x m.
(i)   Find, in terms of t, an expression for x.
(ii) Calculate the smallest positive value of t for which $x = 0.3$.
(iii) Determine, in terms of t, an expression for the rate at which the resultant force acting on the particle is working.

11

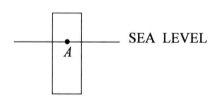

The diagram shows a cylindrical buoy of height 2 m and mass 440 kg floating vertically in a calm sea, the point marked A on the cylinder being at sea level. The upward buoyancy force due to the sea, when the length of the buoy beneath sea level is d m, is $2750d$ N. Find the height of A above the base of the buoy when the buoy is in equilibrium.

(i) The top of the buoy is then moved downwards a distance of 0.2 m at time $t = 0$ s and released from rest. During the subsequent motion the downward displacement of A from sea level at time t s is denoted by x m. Assuming that

    (a) the motion of the buoy can be modelled by the motion of a particle of mass 440 kg at its centre of gravity of the buoy under the action of gravity and the buoyancy force,

    (b) that the motion of the buoy does not affect the sea level,

    show that

$$\frac{d^2x}{dt^2} = -6.25x.$$

(ii) Write down an expression for x in terms of t.

(iii) State the time taken before A first returns to sea level and the maximum speed of the buoy.

(iv) Find the time taken until A is at a depth of 0.1 m below sea level.

A passing ship disturbs the sea level so that at time t s the displacement of the buoy below the level of the calm sea of the sea is $0.4 \sin 2t$. The downward displacement of A below the original level of the calm sea is again denoted by x m. Obtain, but do not attempt to solve, the differential equation satisfied by x.

12

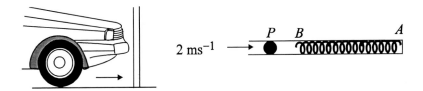

The left hand diagram above shows a car being driven towards a wall in order to test the springing characteristics of a new bumper. The motion of the car can be modelled by the motion of a particle P projected, as in the right hand diagram, towards the free end B of a spring AB free to slide in a smooth horizontal tube, the end A being fixed. The spring is of natural length 0.3 m and modulus of elasticity 72 N. The particle is of mass 0.6 kg and is projected with speed 2 ms^{-1} towards B.

(i) Show that, at time t s after P strikes B, and while P is in contact with B, the compression x m of the spring satisfies

$$\frac{d^2x}{dt^2} = -400x.$$

(ii) Find the maximum compression of the spring and the time taken to achieve that compression.

(iii) Find expressions for the displacement and velocity in terms of t.

(iv) Find the time taken for the speed of P to drop to 1 ms^{-1} for the first time.

(v) What does the model predict about the speed of the car after a time $\frac{\pi}{20}$ s. In what way is this prediction unrealistic?

13 In this question it is assumed that the motion of the water level at the mouth of a harbour can be modelled as a simple harmonic oscillation. The time interval between high tide and low tide is 6.25 hours, at high tide the water depth is 10 m and at low tide it is 7 m. Write down the amplitude and period (in hours) of the oscillation. Measuring time t in hours, with $t = 0$ corresponding to high tide, determine the depth of water at the harbour mouth at time t.

On a particular day the last high tide occurs at 1910 hours. Find the latest time, on that day, that a boat requiring a minimum depth of 9.7 m can enter the harbour.

Determine the rate, in cm per minute, at which the level of water would be falling at that time.

14 A particle is moving in a straight line with simple harmonic motion, O being its centre of oscillation. When the particle is 12 cm from O its speed is 10 cms^{-1} and when the particle is 5 cm from O its speed is 24 cms^{-1}. Find its amplitude and period of oscillation.

If A and B are on opposite sides of O such that $OA = 12$ cm and $OB = 5$cm, find the time taken by the particle to travel directly from A to B.

15 One end A of an elastic string, of natural length a, is held fixed. To the other end B is attached a particle of mass m which hangs freely at a depth of $\frac{6a}{5}$ below A.

The particle is pulled vertically downwards through a distance of $\frac{a}{5}$, held at rest and then released. Write down Newton's equation of motion for the particle when it is at a depth $\frac{6a}{5} + x$ below A during the subsequent motion. Find x as a function of time. What is the periodic time of the motion?

16 A body moves in a straight line so that its displacement x m at time t s is given by

$$x = 3 \cos \pi t + \sin \pi t.$$

Show that the motion is simple harmonic. Find the period and amplitude of the motion.

17 A light string AB obeying Hooke's law is of natural length 1 m and has the end A fixed. When a particle of mass 2 kg is attached to the other end B and allowed to hang, the string is extended by 0.14 m. Find the modulus of elasticity, stating the units in which it is measured.

The particle is pulled down a further 0.2 m then released from rest. Show that until the string becomes slack the motion of the particle is simple harmonic. Show also that the particle passes through the equilibrium position after approximately 0.19 seconds and find the speed of the particle at that time.

18 A particle P of mass m rests on a smooth horizontal plane. Two light horizontal springs AP and BP are attached to P, A and B being fixed points, and APB being a straight line. AB is of length $2a$. Both springs are of natural length a and modulus ka. The system is released from rest at $t = 0$ with $AP = \dfrac{7a}{6}$ and $BP = \dfrac{5a}{6}$. Given that at time t AP is of length $a + y$, derive the equation of motion of P. Hence show that the motion is simple harmonic of period $2\pi\sqrt{\dfrac{m}{2k}}$.

Hence find y in terms of t.

19 One end A of an elastic spring AB is held fixed. When a particle is attached to the spring at B and allowed to hang freely the extension of the spring is 0.2 m. The mass is pulled down vertically through a further small distance and released from rest. Show that the subsequent motion is simple harmonic of period $\dfrac{2\pi}{7}$ s.

20 A particle describes simple harmonic motion along the x-axis with centre at O. When $x = 3$ m the speed (in ms^{-1}) and acceleration (in ms^{-2}) of the particle are equal in magnitude. Given further that the maximum speed of the particle is 2 ms^{-1}, show that the period and the amplitude of the motion are $2\sqrt{3}\pi$ s and $2\sqrt{3}$ m respectively.

21 Two particles A and B move in simple harmonic motion about O with period $2\pi\sqrt{3}$ s and amplitude $2\sqrt{3}$ m. A is released from rest at $t = 0$ s from the extreme point P where $x = 2\sqrt{3}$ m. Particle B is released from P at time $t = \dfrac{\sqrt{3}}{2}\pi$ s. Show that the particles will collide $\dfrac{3\sqrt{3}}{4}\pi$ s after the release of B.

Find how far from O the collision will occur.

22 One end of a light elastic string of natural length a and modulus $2\,mg$ is attached to a fixed point O and the other end to a particle of mass m. The particle, initially at rest at O, is allowed to fall. Find the greatest extension of the string in the motion and show that the particle will again reach O after a time

$$\sqrt{\dfrac{2a}{g}}\left(\pi + 2 - \tan^{-1} 2\right)$$

23 A particle suspended from a fixed point by a light elastic string of natural length l, makes vertical oscillations of amplitude a ($< l$). The modulus of elasticity of the string is equal to the weight of the particle. As the particle rises through its equilibrium position it picks up, from rest, a second particle, also of mass m and the combined masses continue to oscillate. Show that the amplitude of that oscillation is $\sqrt{l^2 + \dfrac{a^2}{2}}$.

24 A body is moving in a straight line with simple harmonic motion. When its distances from the central point are 3 m and 4 m respectively the corresponding speeds are 5 ms^{-1} and 3.75 ms^{-1}. Find the amplitude and period of the motion. Show that the particle takes $\dfrac{2\pi}{15}$ s to move 2.5 m from the central point. At what time after passing through the central point is the speed of the body equal to half its maximum value?

25 A body of mass 2 kg lies on a horizontal platform.
  (i) The platform describes simple harmonic motion vertically of amplitude 0.3 m and period 2 s. Find, in terms of g, the greatest and least forces on the platform due to the body.
  (ii) The platform describes simple harmonic motion horizontally of period 10 s. Given that the greatest speed of the body is $0.12\,\pi$ ms^{-1} and also that it does not slip on the platform, show that the coefficient of friction is greater than $\dfrac{0.024\pi^2}{g}$.

26 A particle of mass m free to move on the x-axis is attracted towards the origin O by a force which is directly proportional to the distance of the particle from O and is resisted by a force which is directly proportional to its speed. Show that at time t s the displacement x m of the particle from O satisfies a differential equation of the form

$$\frac{d^2x}{dt^2} + 2kn\frac{dx}{dt} + n^2 x = 0,$$

where k and n are positive constants.

The particle is projected from O and it is observed that it returns to O at regular intervals. Find the condition that has to be satisfied by k.

The time to travel from one point of instantaneous rest to another is found to be $\dfrac{\pi}{2}$ s.

Show that

$$n^2 (1 - k^2) = 4.$$

It is also observed that the distances from O of successive points where the particle comes to rest are in the ratio 5 to 3. Find the numerical values of k and n.

Chapter 4

Circular Motion

After working through this chapter you should

- be familiar with the expressions for the components of velocity and acceleration for motion in a circle,
- be able to use the above expressions to solve problems involving the motion of a particle moving with constant speed in a horizontal circle; the motion of a car on a banked track is one example of such a motion,
- be able to solve problems of a particle moving in a vertical circle, such problems provide a simple model of fair ground rides such as "loop the loop".

4.1 Basic Kinematics

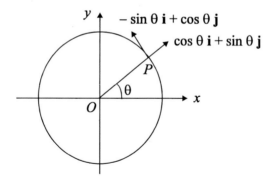

If a particle P moves in a circle of radius r and centre O as shown in the diagram then its position at any time is determined completely by its x- and y- coordinates.

These can be expressed in terms of r and θ, the angle between the radius to the circle and the x-axis giving $x = r \cos \theta$ and $y = r \sin \theta$.

The position vector of the particle can be written as

$$\mathbf{r} = r(\cos \theta \, \mathbf{i} + \sin \theta \, \mathbf{j}),$$

where $\mathbf{i}$ and $\mathbf{j}$ are unit vectors parallel to the x- and y- axes respectively. The angle θ can vary with the time t and $\mathbf{r}$ will therefore also vary with time. The velocity $\mathbf{v}$ is found by differentiating $\mathbf{r}$ with respect to t (remembering that r is constant) i.e.

$$v = \frac{d}{dt}(r(\cos\theta\,\mathbf{i} + \sin\theta\,\mathbf{j})) = r\left(\frac{d\,\cos\theta}{dt}\mathbf{i} + \frac{d\,\sin\theta}{dt}\mathbf{j}\right)$$

$$= r\left(-\sin\theta\frac{d\theta}{dt}\mathbf{i} + \cos\theta\frac{d\theta}{dt}\mathbf{j}\right) = r\frac{d\theta}{dt}(-\sin\theta\,\mathbf{i} + \cos\theta\,\mathbf{j}).$$

The vector $-\sin\theta\,\mathbf{i} + \cos\theta\,\mathbf{j}$ is a unit vector (since $\sin^2\theta + \cos^2\theta = 1$), and, as shown in the diagram, it is perpendicular to OP and in the direction shown in the diagram, that is, it is in the sense of θ increasing.

The velocity is therefore of magnitude $r\frac{d\theta}{dt} = r\dot\theta$ giving the speed v as $r\,|\dot\theta|$, $\dot\theta$ is called the angular velocity and $|\dot\theta|$ the angular speed of the particle. For time measured in seconds the unit of angular speed is rads^{-1}. The normal convention is that the sense of increasing θ is anti-clockwise so that $\dot\theta$ positive refers to an anticlockwise rotation and $\dot\theta$ negative refers to a clockwise rotation.

(Note: Calling $\dot\theta$, which is a scalar, the angular velocity is a simplification to avoid using vectors unnecessarily. Angular velocity is correctly defined as $\dot\theta\,\mathbf{k}$ where $\mathbf{k}$ is a unit vector out of the page. The positive direction of $\mathbf{k}$ is that of the motion of a screw placed vertically on the page and turned anticlockwise. A particle describing a circle in the plane is effectively rotating about an axis perpendicular to the plane and the unit vector $\mathbf{k}$ is in fact along the axis of rotation. For motion in a plane there is only one axis of rotation and introducing $\mathbf{k}$ would tend to complicate expressions. For more general problems such as the motion of a tennis ball in the air, when the motion involves rotation about more than one axis, a vector form has to be used.)

We consider first the case when P has a constant speed, that is, $\dot\theta$ has the constant value ω i.e.

$$\dot\theta = \omega.$$

If $\theta = \alpha$ at time $t = 0$ then integrating the above with respect to t gives $\theta = \alpha + \omega t$, therefore θ will have changed by 2π, i.e. the particle will have returned to its initial position in time $\left|\frac{2\pi}{\omega}\right|$. Therefore the motion is periodic with period T where

$$T = \frac{2\pi}{|\omega|} = \frac{2\pi}{\text{angular speed}}.$$

For $\dot\theta$ constant the expression for v can be differentiated again with respect to t to give the acceleration a and

$$a = \frac{d}{dt}\left(r\frac{d\theta}{dt}(\sin\theta\,\mathbf{i} + \cos\theta\,\mathbf{j})\right) = -r\left(\frac{d\theta}{dt}\right)^2 (\cos\theta\,\mathbf{i} + \sin\theta\,\mathbf{j})$$

$$= -r\,\omega^2\,(\cos\theta\,\mathbf{i} + \sin\theta\,\mathbf{j}).$$

The vector $\cos\theta\,\mathbf{i} + \sin\theta\,\mathbf{j}$ is the unit vector along OP in the sense away from O and therefore the acceleration is directed towards the centre and of magnitude $\omega^2 r$.

Since the speed v is equal to $r\,|\dot\theta| = r\,|\omega|$ the magnitude of the acceleration can be written as $\dfrac{v^2}{r}$.

Summary for motion at constant angular velocity (i.e. constant speed)

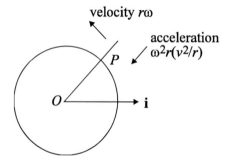

Velocity rω

acceleration $\omega^2 r (v^2/r)$

P

O

$\mathbf{i}$

<u>Velocity</u>
The only component of velocity is perpendicular to the radius vector and its value in the sense of increasing θ is $r\omega$ (see diagram).

<u>Acceleration</u>
The only component is along the radius vector, directed towards the centre and its magnitude is $\omega^2 r = \dfrac{v^2}{r}$ (see diagram).

4.2 Motion at constant speed in a horizontal circle

The above results will now be applied to problems of motion at constant speed in a horizontal circle. The basic equation governing the motion of a particle of mass m under the action of a force $\mathbf{F}$ is,

$$m\mathbf{a} = \mathbf{F},$$

where $\mathbf{a}$ denotes the acceleration $\left(\text{i.e. } \dfrac{d^2\mathbf{r}}{dt^2}\right)$.

The general method of solution is to consider the components of the above equation in particular directions. The most obvious directions for circular motion are along and perpendicular to the radius in the plane of motion and perpendicular to the plane. Since the motion is horizontal there is no acceleration perpendicular to the plane and so the total vertical component of the forces acting will be zero that is, the vertical components of the forces acting are in equilibrium.

If the component acting towards the centre of the total force acting is denoted by F_r then from the results of the previous section,

$$m\omega^2 r = \frac{mv^2}{r} = F_r,$$

where v denotes the speed of the particle and ω denotes its angular speed.

There is no acceleration perpendicular to the radius vector in the plane of motion and, therefore, there can be no force in that direction. This is effectively the basic **modelling assumption** made in assuming motion at constant speed in a horizontal circle i.e. the nett force in the direction of motion is zero. Effectively such a motion assumes that there is no resistance along the path.

It is possible to interpret the above equation as a statical equilibrium equation where the inward force F_r, is balanced by the 'outward' force $m\omega^2 r$, which is referred to as the 'centrifugal' force. We shall not use this approach as it is rather artificial to try and reduce Dynamics to Statics when, in fact, Statics is a particular case of Dynamics! Centrifugal force is effectively a fictitious concept but it can be used, if sufficient care is taken, to solve problems involving circular motion. However the concept of centrifugal force is difficult to generalise to the case of non-uniform motion. It is usually wiser to use Newton's laws for all motion problems without confusing the issue by introducing 'fictitious' forces.

To solve any problem involving motion at constant speed in a horizontal circle all that is necessary to do is

(a) consider vertical equilibrium,

(b) calculate the magnitude of the force F_r acting towards the centre and then use the above equation.

These principles are illustrated in the following examples.

Example 4.1

A particle of mass 1.5 kg is attached to one end of a light string of length 0.2 m and made to describe a circle, at constant speed, on a smooth horizontal table. The string is such that it will break when the tension in it exceeds 2.7 N. Find the maximum angular speed of the particle.

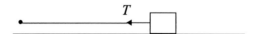

The situation is as shown in the diagram where the only radial force acting on the particle is the tension which is denoted by T N. The radial equation of motion is
$$1.5 \times 0.2\omega^2 = T,$$
where the angular velocity is denoted by ω rads^{-1}.

The maximum value of the tension is 2.7 N which means that maximum value of ω^2 is 9 so that the maximum angular speed is 3 rads^{-1}.

Example 4.2

A particle of mass 0.2 kg is placed at a distance of 0.3 m from the centre of a turntable which can rotate about a vertical axis through its centre. Given that the coefficient of friction between the particle and the turntable is 0.25 find the maximum constant angular speed at which the turntable can rotate without the particle slipping.

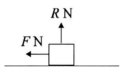

The turntable exerts a normal reaction R N and a frictional force of F N on the particle. Since the particle is moving with constant angular speed the total horizontal force perpendicular to the radius is zero, the only forces that could act being friction and air resistance. Therefore, assuming that air resistance may be neglected, the friction force perpendicular to the radius is zero. Therefore the friction force acts radially as shown in the diagram.

Resolving vertically gives
$$R = 0.2 \times 9.8 = 1.96,$$
and the radial equation of motion is
$$0.2\omega^2 \times 0.3 = F,$$
where the angular speed is denoted by ω rads^{-1}.

The maximum value of $F = 0.25R = 0.49$ and therefore the maximum value of ω satisfies

$$0.06\,\omega^2 = 0.49,$$

giving the maximum value of the angular speed as 2.9 rads^{-1}.

Example 4.3

A car moves without skidding at a constant speed of 25 ms^{-1} in a horizontal circle of radius 125 m. Assuming that there is no friction acting in the direction of motion determine the minimum value of the coefficient of friction.

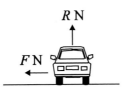

The forces acting on the car are, as shown in the diagram, the friction force F N directed towards the centre of the circle and the vertical reaction R N. The mass of the car will be assumed to be m kg.

The radial equation of motion is

$$m\,\frac{25^2}{125} = F.$$

Resolving vertically shows that

$$R = 9.8\,m.$$

Since $F \leq \mu R$ it follows that

$$\frac{25^2}{125} \leq \mu\,9.8,$$

i.e. $\mu \geq 0.51$.

Example 4.4

Find the maximum speed at which a car could drive round the circle in the previous example if the coefficient of friction were 0.3.

Using the same diagram and notation the radial equation of motion is now

$$m\,\frac{v^2}{125} = F,$$

where the speed is denoted by v ms^{-1}. The expression for R is unchanged and the condition $F \leq 0.3\,R$ shows that $v \leq 19.17$ so that the maximum speed cannot exceed 19.17 ms^{-1}.

Example 4.5

One end of a light elastic string of natural length 0.3 m is attached to a fixed point O on a smooth horizontal table and a particle of mass 0.25 kg is attached to the other end. The particle is made to describe with constant speed 5 ms^{-1}, on the table, a circle of radius 0.4 m and centre O. Find the modulus of elasticity of the string.

The situation is identical to that in the diagram shown in Example 4.1 where the only horizontal force acting is the tension which is denoted by T N. The radial equation of motion is

$$0.25 \times \frac{5^2}{0.4} = T,$$

giving $T = 15.63$.

If the modulus is denoted by λ N then, by Hooke's law, $T = \dfrac{\lambda \times 0.1}{0.3}$ and therefore $\lambda = 46.9$.

Example 4.6

The left hand diagram shows a hollow circular cylinder of radius 0.35 m rotating about its axis and making one revolution per second. A particle of mass 0.2 kg on the inside of the cylinder remains fixed relative to the cylinder throughout the motion. Find the least value of the coefficient of friction between the particle and the cylinder. (This is a simplified model of a particular fairground ride and of the motion in the "wall of death")

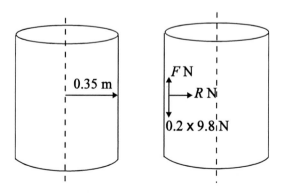

The forces acting on the particle are shown in the right hand diagram with the normal reaction being denoted by R N and the friction force by F N. Since the angular speed is constant there is no horizontal force acting perpendicular to the radius to the particle and therefore the force of friction is vertical.

One revolution per second implies that the particle rotates through 2π radians in one second so that its angular speed is 2π rads^{-1}. The radial equation of motion is
$$R = 0.2 \times 0.35(2\pi)^2 = 2.76.$$
Since the particle is not slipping downwards the nett vertical force must be zero i.e.
$$F = 0.2 \times 9.8 = 1.96.$$
Also for no slipping $F \le \mu R$ and therefore $\mu \ge 0.71$.

Exercises 4.1

Questions 1 to 4 refer to a particle of mass m kg attached to a light string, the other end of which is fixed at a point O. The particle is describing a circle, at constant speed v ms^{-1}, on a smooth horizontal plane through O.

1      $m = 1.5$, the string is inextensible of length 2 m and $v = 9$. Find the tension in the string.

2      $m = 2$ and the string is inextensible of length 3 m and can sustain a maximum force of 400 N without breaking. Find the maximum number of revolutions per second possible without breaking the string.

3      $m = 1.5$ and the string is elastic of unstretched length 0.6 m and modulus 60N. Find the extension if the particle makes 1 complete revolution per second.

4   The string is elastic of unstretched length 0.3 m and, when the particle is suspended from it, is extended a distance 0.02 m. Find the period of revolution when the particle describes a circle of radius 0.34 m at the end of the string.

5   A car travelling on level ground describes a circle of radius 80 m at a speed of 10 ms^{-1}. Find the least value of the coefficient of friction so that the car does not slip.

6   A car is travelling at 10 ms^{-1} on horizontal ground in a circle of radius 30 m. The coefficient of friction between the tyres and the ground is 0.5. Show that the car will not slip.

7   An athlete throwing a hammer swings the hammer at the end of a wire in a horizontal circle of radius 1.8 m. If the hammer makes one revolution per second and weighs 7 kg find the tension in the wire.

8   A particle of mass m is attached to one end of an elastic string of modulus $2mg$ and natural length a. The other end of the string is attached to a point O on a

smooth horizontal table. The particle moves on the table in a circle centre O and radius $1.2a$. Find the angular speed of the particle.

9 A "wall of death" in a fairground consists of a cylinder of radius 8 m. Given that the motor cycle describes horizontal circles and that the coefficient of friction between the motor cycle tyres and the cylinder wall is 0.9 find the least speed so that the motor cycle stays on the wall.

10 A particle of mass m is threaded on a rough horizontal rod which can rotate about a vertical axis through a point O of itself. The particle is attached to O by a light elastic string of modulus 8 mg and natural length a. Given that the coefficient of friction is 0.4, find the maximum angular speed at which the rod can rotate with the particle stationary relative to it and the string of length $1.2\ a$.

4.3 Conical pendulum

A slightly more complicated class of problems arises when considering the motion in a horizontal circle of radius r of a particle attached to the end of a light string, the other end of which is attached to a fixed point vertically above the centre of the circle. The particle describes a circle with constant angular speed ω and the string therefore describes the surface of a cone, hence the term conical pendulum.

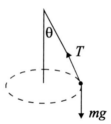

The general situation is illustrated in the diagram above where the string is inclined at an angle θ to the vertical. Taking the particle to be of mass m the equation for vertical equilibrium gives

$$T \cos \theta = mg,$$

whilst the radial component of Newton's law gives

$$T \sin \theta = m\omega^2 r.$$

The above equations govern the motion in any conical pendulum but have to be supplemented by other conditions, depending on the type of problem. In many cases the length l of the string will be given rather than the radius of the circle, so that the relation $a = l \sin \theta$ has to be used. The string may also be elastic, so that the vertical equilibrium equation determines the tension and, therefore, the length of the string.

A further variant occurs when a particle is constrained to move on the surface of a cone. In this case, the normal reaction and, for a rough cone, the tangential reaction have to be taken into account in setting up the basic equations.

In deciding whether a particular motion is possible it is often necessary to use the condition $|\cos\theta| \leq 1$ or $|\sin\theta| \leq 1$.

In all problems, the basic procedure followed should be to mark the forces clearly in a diagram, obtain the equation of vertical equilibrium and the radial equation of motion. If more than one particle is involved then this should be done for each particle. This procedure is illustrated in the following examples. It is safer always to resolve vertically and radially than to use other directions, for example along and perpendicular to the string, as resolving in these latter directions can increase the chance of an algebraic error.

Example 4.7

A particle P of mass 0.5 kg is attached to one end of a light inextensible string of length 0.3 m, the other end of which is held fixed at a point O. P describes, with constant speed, a horizontal circle whose centre is directly below O.

During the motion the string is inclined at an angle of 30° to the vertical. Find the time for one complete revolution of the particle.

The previous diagram can be used with $\theta = 30°$ and the tension, radius of the circle and angular speed will be denoted by T N, r m and ω rads^{-1} respectively.

Resolving vertically gives

$$T\cos 30° = T\frac{\sqrt{3}}{2} = 0.5 \times 9.8,$$

giving $T = \dfrac{9.8}{\sqrt{3}}$.

The radial equation of motion is

$$0.5\,\omega^2 r = T\sin 30° = \frac{1}{2}T,$$

also $r = 0.3\sin 30° = 0.15$ so that $T = 0.15\,\omega^2$.

Therefore $\omega^2 = \dfrac{9.8}{0.15\times\sqrt{3}} = 37.72$, giving $\omega = 6.14$ and the period $\left(\text{i.e.}\,\dfrac{2\pi}{\omega}\right)$ is therefore 1.02 s.

Example 4.8

A particle of mass 0.3 kg is attached to one end of a light elastic string of modulus 23.52 N and natural length 1 m. The other end of the string is attached to a fixed point O and the particle is made to describe, at constant speed, a horizontal circle whose centre is directly below O. The string is of length 1.25 m during this motion.

Find the angular speed of the motion and the angle between the string and the downward vertical.

The previous diagram is still applicable and the tension, radius of the circle and angular speed will again be denoted by T N, r m and ω rads^{-1} respectively.

Resolving vertically gives

$$T \cos \theta = 0.3 \times 9.8 = 2.94.$$

The radial equation of motion is

$$0.3\omega^2 r = T \sin \theta,$$

also $r = 1.25 \sin \theta$ so that

$$T = 0.375 \, \omega^2.$$

The extension of the string is 0.25 m and therefore Hooke's law shows that

$$T = 0.25 \times 23.52 = 5.88$$

and therefore from the equation of vertical equilibrium $\cos \theta = 0.5$ and $\theta = 60°$. Substituting the values for T and θ into the radial equation of motion gives $\omega^2 = 15.68$ so that the angular speed of the particle is 3.96 rads^{-1}.

Example 4.9

Show that for a conical pendulum, with the string being of length l the motion is only possible provided that $g \leq \omega^2 l$.

The basic equations governing the problem are, as found above,

$$T \cos \theta = mg,$$

and

$$T \sin \theta = m\omega^2 r.$$

The radius r is given by $r = l \sin \theta$ so that the radial equation of motion becomes

$$T = m\omega^2 l.$$

Eliminating T shows that

$$\cos \theta = \frac{g}{\omega^2 l},$$

therefore, since $|\cos \theta| \leq 1$, $g \leq \omega^2 l$ thus showing that there is a minimum angular speed necessary for the conical pendulum.

Example 4.10

Determine the minimum value of the modulus of elasticity so that the motion described in Example 4.8 could occur.

If the modulus of elasticity is denoted by λ N then Hooke's law gives

$$T = \frac{\lambda}{4}$$

where λ denotes the elastic modulus and, therefore substituting into $T\cos\theta = 2.94$ gives $\cos\theta = \dfrac{11.76}{\lambda}$. Therefore, since $|\cos\theta| \le 1$, $\lambda \ge 11.76$.

Example 4. 11

A particle describes a horizontal circle with constant angular speed ω on the inner surface of a smooth cone of semi-angle 45°, placed with its vertex O downwards. Find the height above O at which motion takes place.

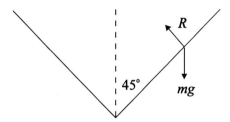

The configuration is as shown in the diagram with R denoting the normal reaction of the cone. Vertical equilibrium gives
$$R\sin 45° = mg,$$
where m is the mass of the particle. The inward force radially is $R\cos 45°$ and, therefore, Newton's law gives
$$R\cos 45° = m\omega^2 r,$$
where r denotes the radius of the circle described by the particle. Eliminating R gives
$$\frac{g}{\omega^2 r} = \tan 45° = 1.$$
The required height h is such that $r = h\tan 45° = h$ and therefore
$$h = \frac{g}{\omega^2}.$$

Example 4.12

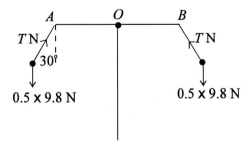

The diagram shows a rod AB, of length 3 m, free to rotate about a vertical axis through its centre O. Light strings each of length 1 m are attached to A and B and each carries a particle of mass 0.5 kg at its end. The rod rotates with constant angular speed so that both strings are inclined at an angle of 30° to the downward vertical. Find the angular speed. (This is a simplified model of a fairground ride often known as the chairoplane)

The forces acting on one of the particles are shown in the diagram with the tension in the string, the radius of the circle described by the particle and angular speed being denoted by T N, r m and ω rads^{-1} respectively.

The equations of motion are effectively the same as in Example 4.4 i.e.

$$T \cos 30° = T \frac{\sqrt{3}}{2} = 0.5 \times 9.8,$$

and

$$0.5\omega^2 r = T \cos 60° = \frac{1}{2} T.$$

The only real difference is that r is now $1.5 + \sin 30° = 2$. From the first equation the value of T is found to be 5.66 and substituting this value of T and the value of r into the second equation gives $\omega^2 = 2.83$ so that the angular speed is 1.68 rads^{-1}.

Problems which are mathematically very similar to those of the conical pendulum are encountered in investigating the banking of roads so as to increase the maximum speed at which a corner may be taken. These problems are discussed in the following section.

Exercises 4.2

Questions 1 to 5 refer to a particle of mass m kg attached to the end of a light string, the other end of which is attached to a point O. The particle describes, with constant speed v ms^{-1}, a horizontal circle in a horizontal plane below O, the centre of the circle being directly below O.

1   The string is inextensible and of length 1.2 m, and is inclined at an angle $\tan^{-1}\left(\dfrac{3}{4}\right)$ to the downward vertical. Find v.

2   $m = 3$, and the string is inextensible and of length 1.6 m. Find the tension in the string when the particle describes 3 revolutions per second.

3   Given that the period of one revolution is 2 s find the distance below O of the circle described by the particle.

4   $m = 4$ and the string is elastic of natural length 0.6 m. Find the modulus, given that when the particle describes 4 revolutions per second the string is of length 0.8 m.

5   $m = 0.5$, the string is elastic of natural length 0.75 m and modulus 100 N, and is inclined at an angle of 30° to the downward vertical. Find the period.

6 A smooth hollow cone is fixed with its axis vertical and vertex downwards. A particle moving on the inner surface of the cone describes a horizontal circle with speed v at a height h above the vertex. Find v in terms of g and h.

7 A smooth hemispherical bowl of inner radius a is placed with its rim uppermost and horizontal. A particle describes a horizontal circle of radius $\dfrac{4a}{5}$ on the inner surface of the bowl. Find the period of revolution of the particle.

8 One end of a light inextensible string of length $5a$ is attached to a fixed point A which is at a distance $3a$ above a smooth horizontal table. A particle of mass m, is attached to the other end of the string and rotates with constant speed in a circle, whose centre is on the table directly below A. Denoting the reaction between the particle and the table by R, find the tension in the string when (i) $R = 0$, (ii) $R = \dfrac{3mg}{4}$.

Find the ratio of the times of revolution for the two cases.

9 A particle of mass m is attached to one end of a light inextensible string of length a. The other end of the string is fixed at a point A which is at a height $\dfrac{3a}{5}$ above a smooth horizontal table. The particle is held on the table with the string taut and projected along the table so that it moves with speed v in a circle. The centre of the circle is directly below A. Show that the reaction of the table on the particle is $m\left(g - \dfrac{15v^2}{16a}\right)$.

10 A circular cone of semi-vertical angle α is fixed with its axis vertical and its vertex A, lowest. A particle P of mass m moves on the smooth inner surface of the cone, which is smooth. The particle is attached to A by a light inextensible string of length a. The particle moves in a horizontal circle with constant speed v and with the string taut. Find the reaction exerted on the particle by the cone.

Determine also the tension in the string and find the condition that $\dfrac{v^2}{ga}$ has to satisfy in order that the motion is possible.

11 A particle is attached by two light inextensible strings of equal length to two points A and B, which are at a distance a apart with A being directly above B. The particle describes a horizontal circle, with its centre on AB, with uniform angular speed ω. Show that $\omega^2 > \dfrac{2g}{a}$ and find the ratio of the tensions in the strings when $\omega^2 = 9\dfrac{g}{a}$.

4.4   Banking of roads and tracks

A car or train moving round a circular bend of a horizontal road or track will have an acceleration towards the centre of the bend and so there must be a force acting on the car towards the centre of the bend. The principal source of such a force is friction. Therefore, on relatively smooth roads this force is small and (since the force is proportional to the square of the speed) the speed at which the car can take a bend without slipping is also relatively low. A typical calculation is given in Example 4.4. If, however, the road is banked, the reaction of the road has a component in the inward direction and the possible maximum speed increases.   Therefore, banking a bend increases the maximum speed at which it can be taken. This principle is also used in flying where an aeroplane banks its wings when turning.

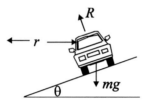

The diagram shows a vehicle of mass m on a bend which is banked at an angle θ to the horizontal, and the vehicle is assumed to be at a point on the road such that it is moving in a horizontal circle of radius r. It can be shown using simple models of rolling that for a vehicle travelling on a road at constant speed there is no friction at the tyres in the direction of motion. We also assume that there is no friction acting along the line of greatest slope of the bank, and the forces acting on the vehicle are therefore the normal reaction R and the force mg due to gravity vertically downwards. The radial component of R is $R \sin \theta$ and therefore the radial equation of motion is

$$R \sin \theta = m \frac{v^2}{r}.$$

Resolving vertically gives

$$R \cos \theta = mg.$$

Eliminating R gives $v^2 = gr \tan \theta$.

The value of v given by this equation is known as the 'self-steering' speed because in theory if the steering wheel had been set properly, a vehicle travelling at this speed would steer round the bend without adjustment.   Present practice is that banking (called super elevation by traffic engineers) should be such that a 'self-steering' vehicle is travelling at the average speed of the traffic using the road.

The idea of using banking so that there is no lateral (i.e. sideways force) is also important in railway design. Since railway wheels are flanged a sideways force is translated into a force on the rail and it obviously useful to minimise this force.   In railway design banking takes the form of setting the outer rail very slightly higher than the inner one.

When a vehicle is going faster than the 'self-steering' speed, there has to be a further force acting inwards. This is provided by friction, whose magnitude is restricted by the value of the coefficient of friction. In practice, the latter has to be determined from empirical data, and using this data, bankings on bends have to be constructed such that the bend can be taken safely up to a certain maximum speed. Typical calculations are shown in Examples 4.17, 4.18 and 4.19. The result $v^2 = gr \tan\theta$ is not one that you would be expected to know and you would normally be expected, in an examination, to derive it. It is likely that quoting it without derivation would actually gain little credit. It will be derived in some of the following but, to avoid repetition, it will sometimes be quoted.

Example 4.13

Find the speed at which a car of mass 1000 kg, moving in a horizontal circle of radius 100 m on a road banked at an angle of 5°, would not experience any lateral force.

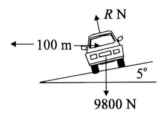

Since there is no lateral force the only forces acting on the car are the normal reaction R N and the vertical force 9800 N due to gravity as shown in the diagram. Resolving vertically gives

$$R \cos 5° = 9800.$$

If the speed is denoted by v ms^{-1} then the radial equation of motion is

$$1000 \frac{v^2}{100} = R \sin 5°.$$

Eliminating R gives

$$v^2 = 980 \tan 5°,$$

and therefore the speed is 9.26 ms^{-1}.

Obviously this is a particular case of the general formula but, as mentioned above, it is a good idea to get into the practice of deriving it from first principles. You should also notice that the same result would have been obtained whatever the mass of the car.

Example 4.14

Find the angle of bank of an aeroplane turning with speed 50 ms^{-1} on a circle of radius 120 m so that, apart from gravity, the only force acting on the aeroplane is the lift which acts perpendicular to the wings. There is therefore no tendency to side-slip. The angle of bank is the angle between the horizontal and the plane of the wings.

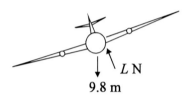

9.8 m

If it is assumed that the aeroplane is of mass m kg then the only forces acting on it are as shown in the diagram, i.e. the lift L N and the weight 9.8 m N.
Resolving vertically gives

$$L \cos \theta = 9.8\, m,$$

where θ is the angle of bank. The radial equation of motion is

$$m \frac{50^2}{120} = L \sin \theta.$$

Eliminating L gives $\tan \theta = \dfrac{50^2}{120 \times 9.8}$ and therefore θ is approximately 64.8°.

Example 4.15

Find by how much the outer rail has to be raised so that a railway truck moving with constant speed 15 ms^{-1} on a horizontal circle of radius 300 m does not exert sideways pressure on the rail. The distance between the rails is 1.48 m.

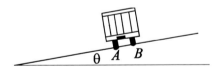

The situation is effectively equivalent to that in the diagram with the truck on a plane inclined at an angle θ to the horizontal and the wheels being in contact at A and B where $AB = 1.48$. The angle θ is determined from the above general result and is given by $\tan \theta = \dfrac{15^2}{300 \times 9.8}$. The height of B above A is $AB \sin \theta = 0.11\text{m}$

Example 4.16

A car of mass 1200 kg travels at a constant speed of 25 ms^{-1} in a horizontal circle of radius 150 m on a track banked at an angle of 20° to the horizontal. Find the lateral force on the car.

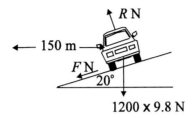

In this case there will be the reaction R N and the lateral (effectively frictional) force F N acting on the car and these forces and the weight are shown in the diagram.

Resolving vertically gives

$$R \cos 20° - F \sin 20° = 1200 \times 9.8 = 11760.$$

The radial equation of motion is

$$R \sin 20° + F \cos 20° = \frac{1200 \times 25^2}{150} = 5000.$$

F can be found by multiplying the second equation by $\cos 20°$ and subtracting from it the first equation multiplied by $\sin 20°$, this gives (using $\cos^2 20° + \sin^2 20° = 1$)

$$F = 5000 \cos 20° - 11760 \sin 20° = 675,$$

the lateral force is therefore 675 N acting down the banking.

The self steering speed for this banking is (using the result $v^2 = gr \tan \theta$) approximately 23 ms^{-1} and as the actual speed is greater than this the force acts down the banking. For speeds less than 23 ms^{-1} the force would act up the banking.

In problems like this where there is both a normal and a lateral force acting an alternative approach, which would avoid the algebra in eliminating F, is to obtain the equations of motion down, and perpendicular to, the banking. This approach is illustrated in Example 4.18 but, unless you are very confident about resolving, it is probably better to stick to resolving vertically and using the radial equation of motion.

Example 4.17

Find the maximum speed at which the motion in the previous problem would be possible without the car slipping up the banking given that the coefficient of friction between the car and the banking is 0.5.

The first equation will be unchanged and, if the speed is taken as v ms^{-1}, the 25 will have to be replaced by v. The equations are therefore

$$R \cos 20° - F \sin 20° = 1200 \times 9.8 = 11760,$$

and $$R \sin 20° + F \cos 20° = \frac{1200 \times v^2}{150} = 8v^2.$$

F can be found as before and

$$F = 8v^2 \cos 20° - 11760 \sin 20°.$$

It is now necessary to find R. This is done by multiplying the first equation by cos 20° and the second equation by sin 20° and adding the equations.

This gives, on using $\cos^2 20° + \sin^2 20° = 1$,

$$R = 8v^2 \sin 20° + 11760 \cos 20°.$$

The maximum value of v can be found by using the condition $F \leq 0.5\,R$,

i.e. $$8v^2 \cos 20° - 11760 \sin 20° \leq 0.5\,(8v^2 \sin 20° + 11760 \cos 20°),$$

or $$v^2\,(8 \cos 20° - 4 \sin 20°) + 11760 \sin 20° + 5880 \cos 20°.$$

This gives the maximum speed as 39.4 ms^{-1}.

Example 4.18

A road is to be banked so that a car moving with a speed of 25 ms^{-1} in a circular bend of radius 125 m can travel without skidding. The coefficient of friction is 0.3.
Find the least possible angle of banking.

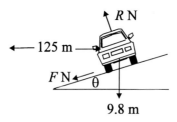

The car is assumed to be of mass m *kg* and the forces acting, and shown in the diagram, are the normal reaction R N, the friction force F N acting down the banking and the weight 9.8 m N acting vertically downwards. The acceleration of the car is $\frac{25^2}{125}$ ms^{-2} = 5ms^{-2} acting horizontally and the component of this perpendicular to the banking and in the same sense as R is 5 sin θ ms^{-2}. Similarly the component of the acceleration down the banking and in the same sense as F is 5 cos θ ms^{-2}. The components of the equation of motion normal to and down the banking are

$$R - 9.8\,m \cos θ = 5\,m \sin θ,$$

and $$F + 9.8\,m \sin θ = 5\,m \cos θ.$$

Taking components down, and perpendicular to, the banking has avoided the algebraic elimination used in the previous two examples.

The condition $F \leq 0.3 R$ gives
$$5 \, m \cos \theta - 9.8 \, m \sin \theta \leq 0.3(9.8 \, m \cos \theta + 5 \, m \sin \theta),$$
i.e. $\qquad\qquad 11.3 \tan \theta \geq 2.06.$

The minimum banking angle is therefore approximately 10.3°.

Example 4.19

Show that, if the coefficient of friction is 0.2, then it would not be possible for a car to stay at rest on a road banked at an angle of 30° and find the least speed such that, with this angle of banking, a car could move in a horizontal circle of radius 100 m.

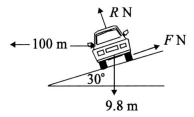

The forces acting on the car are the normal reaction R N, the friction force F N acting down (or up) the banking and the force of gravity $9.8 \, m$ N if the car is taken to be of mass m kg. Since the car is initially assumed at rest the force of friction is assumed to act up the banking otherwise equilibrium is not possible.

Resolving up, and perpendicular to, the banking gives
$$F = 9.8 \, m \sin 30°$$
and $\qquad\qquad R = 9.8 \, m \cos 30°.$

Therefore
$$\frac{F}{R} = \tan 30° = 0.58.$$

This is greater than the coefficient of friction and so the car would slide down. If it is assumed that the car moves with speed v ms^{-1} then taking the components of the equation of motion up, and perpendicular to, the banking, as shown in the previous example, gives
$$R - 9.8 \, m \cos 30° = m \frac{v^2}{100} \sin 30°,$$
and $\qquad -F + 9.8 \, m \sin 30° = m \frac{v^2}{100} \cos 30°.$

Using the condition $F \leq 0.2R$ gives
$$9.8 \sin 30° - \frac{v^2}{100} \cos 30° \leq 0.2 \left(9.8 \cos 30° + \frac{v^2}{100} \sin 30° \right)$$

and

$$\frac{v^2}{100}(\cos 30° + 0.2 \sin 30°) \geq 9.8(\sin 30° - 0.2 \cos 30°).$$

The minimum speed is therefore 18.2 ms^{-1}.

Exercises 4.3

1   A car of mass 1000 kg is moving round a circular track which is banked at an angle $\tan^{-1} 0.2$ to the horizontal. The car is travelling in a circle of radius 600 m at a speed of 30 ms^{-1}. Find the lateral force acting on it.

2   A road is banked at an angle of 10° to the horizontal at a bend of radius 90 m. At what speed should a car travel round the bend so that there would be no lateral friction force between the tyres and the ground?

3   At what angle should an aircraft flying at 200 ms^{-1} be banked so that it moves, without side slipping, in a horizontal circle of radius 2 km?

4   A circular track of radius 300 m is banked at an angle of 45°. Given that the coefficient of friction between the wheels and the ground is 0.4 find the maximum speed at which a car can travel round the track without side slipping.

5   A railway curve is an arc of a circle of radius r and the track is banked at an angle α so that there is no lateral force on the rails when the train is moving at speed v. Find the lateral force when a train of mass m goes round the curve at speed $1.5v$.

6   The maximum speed at which a car can travel, without skidding, round a circular bend of radius 120 m which is banked at an angle of 10° is 25 ms^{-1}. Find the coefficient of friction.

7   Find the angle at which a circular bend of radius 100 m has to be banked so that the maximum speed at which a car can travel, without skidding, round the bend is 20 ms^{-1}. The coefficient of friction is 0.25.

8   A car describes a horizontal circle of radius 100 m at 18 ms^{-1} on a track which is banked at an angle α to the horizontal. Determine $\tan \alpha$ so that there is no lateral force acting on the car. Find, for this value of α, the least coefficient of friction such that the car can go round the track without slipping at a speed of 28 ms^{-1}.

9   A car can travel on a level road round a bend of radius 50 m at a maximum speed of 15 ms^{-1} without slipping. Find, assuming that the coefficient of friction would be unchanged, the angle at which the road should be banked so that the car could travel round the bend without slipping at a speed of 20 ms^{-1}.

10   A circular track of radius 250 m is banked at an angle of 20°. Given that the coefficient of friction between the wheels and the ground is 0.3 find the range of speeds at which a car can travel round the track without side slipping.

4.5   Circular motion and simple harmonic motion

We now examine very briefly the relationship between circular motion and simple harmonic motion which was mentioned in 3.1.

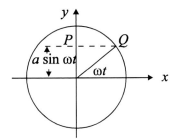

The diagram shows a point Q describing in the counter clockwise sense a circle of centre O and radius a with angular speed ω. If θ denotes the angle between OQ and the x-axis then

$$\frac{d\theta}{dt} = \omega.$$

Integrating this with respect to t gives $\theta = \omega t + c$, where c is a constant. If Q is at the point $\theta = 0$ for $t = 0$ the constant is zero so that $\theta = \omega t$. The perpendicular from Q to the y-axis intersects it at the point P, which is referred to as the projection of Q on the y-axis. The y coordinate of P is therefore $a \sin \theta = a \sin \omega t$. Therefore the point P describes simple harmonic motion, centre O, amplitude a and period $\dfrac{2\pi}{\omega}$.

In unit time the angle θ increases by ω and this is therefore the number of radians described per unit time, hence the term natural circular frequency.

If Q had been at the point corresponding to $\theta = \varepsilon$ at time $t = 0$ then the constant c would be ε and then $\theta = \omega t + \varepsilon$ and the y coordinate of P would then be $a \sin (\omega t + \varepsilon)$.

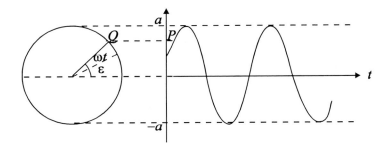

This is the general form of displacement in simple harmonic motion and therefore the motion of the projection on a diameter of a particle describing a circle is simple harmonic. The diagram illustrates the behaviour of P as Q describes the circle. Equivalently any problem involving simple harmonic motion can be translated into one on motion in a circle with constant angular speed. Effectively the problem is translated from one involving algebra and the use of solutions of differential equations to one in geometry and you might find this harder. Also most examination questions tend to be phrased in such a way that full credit will only be given if the methods described in the previous chapter are used.

The alternative and more geometric approach is illustrated in the following example.

Example 4.20

A particle describes simple harmonic motion with amplitude 2 m and period 18 s. Find the time taken to travel directly from a point a distance of 1 m from the centre to one at a distance of $\sqrt{3}$ m from the centre.

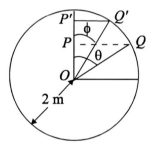

The two points are denoted by P and P' and they are the projections onto the line of motion of the points Q and Q' on the circle of radius 2 m. θ and ϕ denote the angles between the line of motion and OQ and OQ', respectively.

$OP = 2 \cos \theta = 1$ and $OP' = 2 \cos \phi = \sqrt{3}$ so that $\theta = \dfrac{\pi}{3}$ and $\phi = \dfrac{\pi}{6}$.

The angle between OQ and OQ' is therefore $\dfrac{\pi}{6}$. This is $\dfrac{1}{12}$ of the total angle in a circle (i.e. 2π) and therefore the time taken to travel from P to P' is a twelfth of the period i.e. 1.5 s.

4.6 Kinematics for motion with variable speed

It was shown in 4.1 that the velocity v of a particle moving in a circle of radius r was given by

$$v = r\frac{d\theta}{dt}(-\sin \theta\, \mathbf{i} + \cos \theta\, \mathbf{j}),$$

where θ, $\mathbf{i}$ and $\mathbf{j}$ are defined in 4.1 and shown in the following diagram.

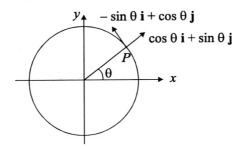

The acceleration a is found, as in 4.1, by differentiating v with respect to t. In this case, however, $\dfrac{d\theta}{dt}$ is not constant and its derivative has to be included.

Therefore

$$a = \frac{d}{dt}\left(r\frac{d}{dt}(-\sin\theta\mathbf{i} + \cos\theta\mathbf{j})\right) = -r\left(\frac{d\theta}{dt}\right)^2 (\cos\theta\,\mathbf{i} + \sin\theta\,\mathbf{j}) + r\frac{d^2\theta}{dt^2}(-\sin\theta\,\mathbf{i} + \cos\theta\,\mathbf{j}).$$

The first term above is of magnitude $r\left(\dfrac{d\theta}{dt}\right)^2$ directed radially inwards and the

second is of magnitude $r\dfrac{d^2\theta}{dt^2}$ directed along the tangent in the direction of θ

increasing. Also

$$r\frac{d^2\theta}{dt^2} = \frac{d(r\dot\theta)}{dt} = \frac{dv}{dt} = \dot v.$$

Therefore in circular motion when the speed is not constant there are two components of acceleration,

$\qquad$ (i) $r\dot\theta^2 = \dfrac{v^2}{r}$ directed radially inwards

and $\qquad$ (ii) $r\ddot\theta = \dot v$ along the tangent in the sense of θ increasing.

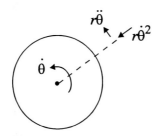

These expressions will now be used in the following section to investigate problems involving motion in a vertical circle.

4.7 Motion in a vertical circle

So far the only problems examined are those when the only force in the plane of motion is radial so that the angular speed remains constant. We now consider a class of problems - those involving motion in a vertical circle - where the angular speed is not constant.

Typical problems which can be modelled as a particle moving in a vertical circle are the motion of a particle whirled at the end of a string (or a bucket of water being whirled in a vertical circle) and the motion of a car in a roller coaster. The problems are mathematically very similar but the interpretation of the results vary.

The methods to be used will be illustrated by using as a prototype problem that of the motion of a particle threaded on a smooth vertical circular loop of wire.

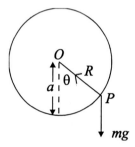

The diagram shows a vertical circular wire of centre O and radius a on which a bead P of mass m is threaded. The angle between OP and the downward vertical is denoted by θ. The wire is assumed to be smooth so that the only force that it exerts on P is radial and of magnitude R and this is shown in the diagram acting radially inwards. The only other force acting on P is the force of gravity vertically downwards which has a component $mg \cos\theta$ acting outwards and a component $mg\sin\theta$ tangentially in the direction of decreasing θ. The components of the acceleration of P radially inwards and tangentially are $a\dot\theta^2$ and $a\ddot\theta$.

The radial and tangential components of Newton's law give

$$R - mg \cos\theta = m\,a\dot\theta^2,$$

$$m\,a\ddot\theta = -mg\sin\theta.$$

The second equation is the differential equation relating θ to t, and the first step is to try and integrate this equation. One method is to multiply both sides of the equation by $\dot\theta$ giving

$$ma\ddot\theta\,\dot\theta = -mg\sin\theta\,\dot\theta.$$

Also
$$\ddot\theta\,\dot\theta = \frac{1}{2}\frac{d\dot\theta^2}{dt} \quad\text{and}\quad \sin\theta\,\dot\theta = -\frac{d\cos\theta}{dt}$$

so that the equation of motion becomes

$$ma\frac{1}{2}\frac{d\dot\theta^2}{dt} = mg\frac{d\cos\theta}{dt}.$$

This equation can be integrated to give

$$\frac{1}{2}ma\dot\theta^2 = mg\cos\theta + \text{constant}.$$

An alternative method of carrying out the above integration is to use

$$\ddot\theta = \frac{d\dot\theta}{dt} = \frac{d\dot\theta}{d\theta}\dot\theta \quad \text{(applying the chain rule)},$$

$$= \frac{1}{2}\frac{d\dot\theta^2}{dt}$$

If it is assumed that P has a speed u $\left(\text{i.e. } \dot\theta = \dfrac{u}{a}\right)$ at its lowest point A (when $\theta = 0$),

the constant can be found by substituting into the expression for $\dot\theta^2$ giving

$$a^2\dot\theta^2 = u^2 + 2ag(\cos\theta - 1).$$

This equation could also have been obtained by using conservation of energy, this is actually the most direct method and will be considered below.

The value of $\dot\theta$ can now be substituted into the equation for R giving

$$R = \frac{mu^2}{a} + mg(3\cos\theta - 2).$$

The basic problem has now been solved and it now remains to interpret it. The interpretation varies with the type of problem but before going any further it is worth looking at the use of energy conservation.

Energy Conservation

It can be proved that

Kinetic energy + Potential energy due to gravity

    + Elastic energy (if an elastic string is involved) = Work done by other forces.

A proof is given in M2 for one dimensional motion but it is possible, by using the work energy principle, to prove the above result. You will not be expected to derive a proof as some of the mathematics necessary is not covered in your course.

In the case of the bead threaded on the wire the only other force acting is the reaction. The wire is smooth so the reaction is always perpendicular to the direction of motion and the work done by it is therefore zero. Therefore the total energy is conserved.

The work done by the tension in an inextensible string is also zero and energy is again conserved.

We return now to the problem of the bead on the wire. The potential energy, taking the potential energy to be zero at the level of the centre of the circle, is $-mga\cos\theta$. The kinetic energy is $\frac{1}{2}mv^2$, where v denotes the speed, and therefore conservation of energy gives

$$\frac{1}{2}mv^2 - ga\cos\theta = \text{constant}.$$

This, when you remember that $v = |a\dot\theta|$, is the equation found by integrating the radial equation of motion. Using energy conservation avoids having to integrate the equation of motion directly.

Interpretation of results

The basic results are

$$a^2\dot\theta^2 = u^2 + 2ag(\cos\theta - 1),$$

and
$$R = \frac{mu^2}{a} + mg(3\cos\theta - 2).$$

If $\theta = \pi$ is substituted into the equation for $\dot\theta^2$ this gives its value at the highest point as $u^2 - 4ag$. If $u^2 < 4ag$ this expression will be negative meaning that the particle will not reach the highest point and will just oscillate on either side of the vertical through the centre.

There are five slightly different problems involving motion in a vertical circle: a particle whirled at the end of a string, a particle moving on the inside or outside of a smooth circle, a particle threaded on a bead or attached to the end of a thin rod (the last two are effectively the same). The main difference between the problems is the way in which the motion breaks down (i.e. whether the string becomes slack or breaks and whether the particle comes off the circular path). The problems of the threaded bead and rod are slightly different in that the motion cannot break down other than by the wire or rod collapsing.

Particle on inside of a cylinder

For a particle on on the inside of a cylinder the motion will be as shown in the above diagram with the reaction R inwards and so the expression for R must always be positive. For $\theta = \pi$, R is equal to $u^2 - 5ag$. If $u^2 < 5ag$ the particle will drop off the cylinder, and the particle will move as a projectile for a while. The actual value of θ at which the break down occurs is found by setting $R = 0$.

Particle on an inextensible string

This problem is mathematically identical to that of a particle on the inside of a cylinder. The reaction R has to be replaced by the tension T of the string. The string will become slack when, as above, $u^2 < 5ag$.

Particle on outside of cylinder

The forces acting on a particle at the lowest point on the outside of a cylinder will all be downwards and, as you would expect, the particle drops down. Therefore, in this case, it is not sensible to project a particle from the lowest point with speed u and different initial conditions have to be used. The equations of motion could be obtained by replacing R by $-R$ above but, in order to get more practice, it seems better to start again.

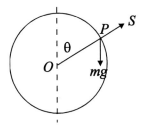

The diagram shows a vertical section of a circular cylinder centre O and radius a on which a particle P of mass m can move. The angle between OP and the upward vertical is denoted by θ. (When OP is horizontal the horizontal force acting on it is outwards and its horizontal acceleration is inwards. This is an impossible situation and therefore the particle will have dropped off before reaching this position. It is better to use the angle with the upward vertical since θ will always acute.) Since the cylinder is smooth the reaction of the cylinder will be radially outwards and denoted by S. The radial equation of motion is

$$mg \cos \theta - S = ma\dot\theta^2,$$

the potential energy (taking the potential energy to be zero at the level of O) is $mga \cos \theta$.

Conservation of energy gives

$$\frac{1}{2} mv^2 + mga \cos \theta = \text{constant}.$$

If the speed of the particle at the top is assumed to be U $(U^2 < ga)$, then the constant is $\frac{1}{2} mU^2 + mga$ so that

$$v^2 = U^2 + 2ga (1 - \cos \theta).$$

This becomes, using $v = |a\dot\theta|$,

$$a^2\dot\theta^2 = U^2 + 2ga(1 - \cos\theta).$$

Substituting in the radial equation gives

$$S = 3mg\cos\theta - 2mg - \frac{mU^2}{a}.$$

Substituting $\theta = 0$ in this equation for S gives $S = mg - \frac{mU^2}{a}$, and the restriction on

U means that this is positive so that there is a positive reaction at the highest point and the particle will not fly off.

If $U^2 > ga$ then S would be negative for $\theta = 0$ and the particle would just fly off at the top of the cylinder.

For $\theta = \frac{\pi}{2}$, S will be negative so the particle will fall off before getting to the level of the centre of the cylinder, as predicted above. The actual value of θ at which this happens is found by setting $S = 0$ and solving for θ, this gives

$$\cos\theta = \frac{U^2}{3ga} + \frac{2}{3}.$$

Problem solving

The first step is, as usual, to show in a diagram the forces acting and, in particular, to make sure that (when relevant) they are in the physically sensible sense (for example the tension in a string is always radially inwards). Once the forces have been determined the next step is to write down the radial equation of motion and the equation of conservation of energy. It is very important to use your initial conditions carefully in order to find the constant in the energy equation. In many cases it is simpler to use speed rather than angular speed, particularly if you are given information about speeds or asked to find speeds. In such cases you use the radial acceleration in the form $\frac{v^2}{r}$. The expression obtained for $\dot\theta^2$ or v^2 can then be used to express the radial force in terms of θ.

An alternative to using conservation of energy is to obtain the tangential equation of motion and integrate it as above. This method has the snag of making errors more likely.

In harder problems where you are uncertain that energy is conserved (if for example friction is involved) you will have to use the tangential equation of motion and attempt to integrate it using $\ddot\theta = \frac{d\dot\theta}{dt} = \frac{d\dot\theta}{d\theta}\dot\theta$. You may also need to use the tangential equation when more than one particle is involved.

You then have to try and interpret the results for your particular problem. The variations in the type of problems that can occur are produced almost entirely by varying the way in which the particle is constrained. If for example the particle is attached to the end of a light inextensible string (or moves on the inside of a smooth cylinder) then motion is only possible for positive values of the tension (or reaction) and the conditions for the motion to be possible, or the value of θ for which the motion ceases to be possible (that is the particle leaves the circle), are often sought. Similar problems occur for motion on the outer surface of a cylinder or sphere. The reaction in this case is outward and the condition for a positive reaction may have to be applied to determine whether or not the motion is feasible.

You may also be required in particular cases to determine whether or not complete revolutions are described. The smallest value of $\dot{\theta}^2$ occurs at the highest point of the circle and for complete revolutions this has to be positive. It is of course necessary to make certain first that the motion has not already ceased to be possible before reaching this position.

Example 4.21

A child of mass 25 kg is on a swing and swings freely through an angle of 30° on either side of the vertical. The ropes of the swing are 2 m long. Assuming that the motion of the child can be modelled by that of a particle of mass 25 kg attached to an inextensible rope of length 2 m, find the speed of the child when the rope is vertical and also the tension in the rope at that instant.

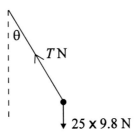

The diagram shows the motion when the rope is at an angle θ to the vertical with the tension in the rope being denoted by T N and acting inwards.

The radial equation of motion is

$$T - 25 \times 9.8 \cos \theta = 25 \frac{v^2}{r}.$$

The equation of conservation of energy is

$$\frac{1}{2} \times 25v^2 - 25 \times 9.8 \times 2 \cos \theta = \text{constant}.$$

The swing stops at 30° on either side of the vertical so $v = 0$ for $\theta = 30°$ so that the constant is $-25 \times 9.8 \times 2 \cos 30°$ and therefore

$$\frac{1}{2} \times 25v^2 = 25 \times 9.8 \times 2(\cos\theta - 30°)$$

The value of the speed at the lowest point can be found by substituting $\theta = 0$ into the equation of energy giving the speed as 2.29 ms^{-1}.

Substituting this value of the speed into the radial equation of motion for $\theta = 0$ gives the tension as 311 N.

Example 4.22

A particle of mass m free to move on the inner surface of a smooth hollow cylinder of internal radius $2a$ is projected from the lowest point of the cylinder with a horizontal speed of magnitude $\sqrt{2ga}$. Determine the maximum height that the particle rises above the point of projection.

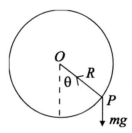

The forces acting are as shown in the diagram. The radial equation of motion is

$$R - mg \cos\theta = 2ma\dot\theta^2,$$

and the equation of conservation of energy is

$$\frac{1}{2}m(2a)^2 \dot\theta^2 - 2mga \cos\theta = \text{constant.}$$

The speed when $\theta = 0$ is $\sqrt{2ga} = 2a\dot\theta$ and substituting these values in the energy equation shows that the constant is $-mga$ so that

$$2a^2\dot\theta^2 = ga(2\cos - 1).$$

$\dot\theta$ vanishes when $\cos\theta = \frac{1}{2}$ so that the greatest height $(2a - 2a\cos\theta)$ reached above the lowest point is a. In this case it is obvious that R is positive when θ is acute and so the particle does not leave the cylinder before reaching the above position.

Example 4.23

A particle P of mass m is free to move on the outer surface of a smooth circular cylinder of radius a, and is released from rest at a depth of $\dfrac{a}{10}$ below the highest point.

Find the height above the centre of the cylinder of the point at which P leaves the cylinder.

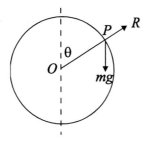

The situation is shown in the diagram with R denoting the reaction of the cylinder acting outwards. The radial equation of motion is

$$mg \cos \theta - R = ma\dot{\theta}^2,$$

and the equation of conservation of energy is

$$\frac{1}{2} ma^2 \dot{\theta}^2 + mga \cos \theta = \text{constant}.$$

Initially, $\dot{\theta} = 0$ when $\cos \theta = \dfrac{9}{10}$ so that the constant is equal to $\dfrac{9mga}{10}$. Therefore,

$$5ma^2 \dot{\theta}^2 + 10mga \cos \theta = 9mga.$$

Substituting for $\dot{\theta}$ in the radial equation of motion gives

$$5R = 15 \, mg \cos \theta - 9mg.$$

The reaction vanishes when $\cos \theta = \dfrac{3}{5}$, that is, when P is at a distance $\dfrac{2a}{5}$ above the centre.

Modelling a real situation

If a round circular cake tin was placed on its side and a small particle placed at the top and gently disturbed then this problem could be modelled by that of a particle set off from rest from the top of a circular cylinder. The situation is exactly as in the previous example and the radial equation of motion is unchanged. Since the particle is released from rest from the highest point (you actually have to assume that it is given a small velocity otherwise it will not move!) the constant in the equation of energy is now mga so that

$$\frac{1}{2} ma^2 \dot{\theta}^2 + mga \cos \theta = mga.$$

Substituting in the radial equation gives

$$R = 3mg \cos \theta - 2mg - \frac{mU^2}{a}.$$

For a particle just disturbed from rest $U = 0$ and therefore the particle would leave the cylinder when the radius had turned through an angle θ where $\cos \theta = \frac{2}{3}$

i.e. $\theta = 48.2°$.

In practice modelling a particle sliding would not be particularly accurate as friction would have to be taken into account. However a marble rolling could be modelled relatively accurately by a particle sliding on a smooth surface since the friction at the point of contact does no work. For a marble rolling with speed v the kinetic energy can be shown to be $\frac{7}{10} mv^2$ and using this value the equation of conservation of energy becomes

$$7v^2 = 10ga (1 - \cos \theta).$$

Substituting in the radial equation of motion i.e.

$$mg \cos \theta - R = m \frac{v^2}{a},$$

gives $$R = mg \left(\frac{17}{7} \cos \theta - \frac{10}{7} \right).$$

The reaction vanishes for $\cos \theta = \frac{10}{17}$ giving $\theta = 53°$.

Exercises 4.4

Questions 1 to 4 refer to a particle, describing a vertical circle, attached to one end of a light inextensible string of length a.

1 Given that the speed at the highest point is $8\sqrt{ga}$, find the speed at the lowest point.

2 Find the speed with which the particle is projected from the lowest point so that it describes semi-circles.

3 Given that the particle is of mass 0.2 kg, $a = 0.4$ m and the tension when the string is inclined at an angle 60° to the downward vertical is 15 N, find the speed at the lowest point.

4 Given that $a = 0.5$ m and that the greatest and least tensions are in the ratio 3 to 1, find the greatest speed of the particle.

5 An aeroplane is flown at a constant speed of 180 ms⁻¹ in a vertical circle of radius 1200 m. Find the force exerted by the seat on the pilot, of mass 75 kg, at the lowest and highest points.

6   A man swings a bucket full of water in a vertical plane in a circle of radius 0.4 m. What is the smallest velocity that the bucket should have at the top of the circle if no water is to be spilt.

7

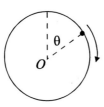

The diagram shows a cylinder of radius 0.35 m rotating about its axis, which is horizontal, with constant angular speed ω. A particle of mass m on the inner surface of the cylinder is rotating without slipping relative to the cylinder. The coefficient of friction between the particle and the cylinder is μ. Find the condition to be satisfied by ω if the particle has not slipped at the position shown.

8   A bead of mass m is threaded on a smooth circular loop of wire of radius a which is fixed in a vertical plane. The bead is released from rest at the end of a horizontal diameter. Find the reaction of the wire when the bead has turned through an angle θ.

9   A particle is released from rest on the surface of a smooth sphere of radius a at a height $\dfrac{a}{2}$ above the centre of a smooth sphere of radius a. Find the height above the centre at which the particle leaves the sphere.

10   A particle of mass m is free to slide on a circular wire hoop of radius a in a vertical plane. The wire is such that, once the particle is set in motion, it experiences a force of constant magnitude $3mg$ opposing its motion. The particle is projected from the lowest point of the wire and it comes to instantaneous rest opposite the centre of the wire. Find the speed of projection.

Miscellaneous Exercises 4

1   A fixed point O is at a height h above a smooth horizontal table and one end of a light inextensible string is fixed at O and a particle P, of mass m, is attached to the other end. The particle is made to describe a circle on the table, with constant angular speed ω, and with the string taut. The centre of the circle is directly below O. Find, in terms of m, g, ω and h, the magnitude of the reaction of the table. Determine the greatest value of ω^2 for which such a motion is possible.

The table is then removed and the inextensible string replaced by a light elastic string of modulus mg and natural length a. The particle P is then constrained to describe horizontal circles, with centre directly below O with constant angular speed Ω. Denoting the tension in the string by T, find an expression for the length of the string

(i) in terms of T, m, g and a, (ii) in terms of T, m and Ω.

Hence find T in terms of m, g, a and Ω.

2   A particle of mass m is attached to one end of a light inextensible string of length a whose other end is attached to a fixed point O. Initially the particle is held at rest at a point B with the string taut and OB inclined at an angle $\dfrac{\pi}{3}$ to the downward vertical through O.

(a)   The particle is projected horizontally with speed u from B so that it describes, with constant speed, a horizontal circle whose centre lies on the vertical through O. Find u and the time taken to describe one complete circle.

(b)   The particle is projected from B, perpendicular to OB in the vertical plane containing OB with speed w so that it starts describing a vertical circle, centre O.

Find the tension in the string when it is inclined at an angle θ to the downward vertical. Find also the least value of w so that the particle describes complete circles.

3   A particle of mass m is suspended from a fixed point A by an elastic string of natural length b and modulus λ. The particle describes a horizontal circle with angular speed ω with the string being of constant length $l\ (> b)$, the centre of the circle being directly below A.

Given that the angle between the string and the downward vertical is θ, show that

$$\cos \theta = \frac{g}{l\omega^2}.$$

The breaking tension in the string is $10mg$ and it is found that this occurs when $b\omega^2 = 9g$. Find $\cos \theta$ when the string breaks and express λ in terms of m and g.

4   A particle of mass m is attached by a light inextensible string of length l to the vertex of a cone of semi-vertical angle α. The cone is fixed with its axis vertical and vertex upwards and the particle moves in a horizontal circle on the smooth outside surface of the cone with angular speed ω. Find expressions for the reaction R between the cone and the particle, and the tension T in the string.

Find the greatest possible value of ω in terms of g, l and α if the particle is to remain on the cone.

Suppose now that the string is elastic of natural length a and modulus $3mg$, $\alpha = \tan^{-1}\left(\dfrac{3}{4}\right)$ and that $\omega^2 = \dfrac{g}{2a}$. Find the extension of the string.

5   The maximum speed at which a car can travel around a horizontal circular bend of radius 120 m without skidding is 30 ms^{-1}. Find the coefficient of friction between the wheels of the car and the road. Calculate the least angle at which the road should be banked in order that the car can negotiate the bend without skidding at 50 ms^{-1}, assuming that the coefficient of friction remains unchanged.

6   A car travels, without skidding, at 63 km h^{-1} round a circular bend of radius 80 m on a horizontal surface. Show that the coefficient of friction between the wheels and the road is at least $\dfrac{25}{64}$.

7

The diagram shows a car of mass m travelling at constant speed in a horizontal circle of radius a on a road banked at an angle α to the horizontal. The coefficient of friction between the car and the road is 0.6 and $\sin \alpha = \dfrac{5}{13}$. The car may be modelled as a particle of mass m moving in a horizontal circle of radius a. Given that the car is on the point of sliding up the bank

(a) show, by resolving vertically, that the normal reaction of the road on the car is $\dfrac{13mg}{9}$,

(b) find, in terms of g and a, the speed of the car.

8   In some amusement parks there is a ride which is effectively an open cylinder which can rotate about a vertical axis. The riders stand on the base of the cylinder but against the surface of the cylinder. When the angular speed reaches a certain value the floor is dropped but the riders remain stuck to the surface of the cylinder. The radius of the cylinder is 2.5 m and the speed of rotation is 30 revolutions per minute. Find the smallest possible coefficient of friction between the rider and the cylinder surface so that the ride works effectively.

9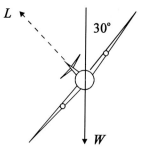

An aircraft, in order to travel in a circle, has to bank (i.e. tilt so that the wings are at an angle to the vertical). The diagram shows an aircraft, banked at an angle of 30° to the vertical, travelling in a horizontal circle, at constant height. The only forces acting in the plane perpendicular to the direction of motion of the aircraft are the lift L, perpendicular to the wings, and the weight W as shown. The aircraft is of mass 1200 kg and <u>is moving with constant speed 60 ms^{-1}</u>.

(a) Modelling the aircraft as a particle find

    (i) the lift,

    (ii) the radius of the circle in which the aircraft is moving.

(b) The words underlined above imply a modelling assumption about the forces acting on the aircraft in the direction of its motion. State what you think this modelling assumption to be.

10 A particle P of mass m is placed at the highest point on the outside of a fixed smooth hollow sphere of radius a and centre O. The particle P is just disturbed from rest. Assuming that P remains in contact with the sphere, show that the reaction of the sphere on P is

$$mg\,(3\cos\theta - 2),$$

where θ is the angle between the upward vertical and the radius OP.

Write down the value of $\cos\theta$ at the point where P leaves the sphere.

A particle Q, on the inside of the sphere is projected horizontally from the lowest point of the sphere with speed u. Find u, in terms of a and g, so that both P and Q leave the surface of the sphere at the same height above O.

11 A smooth loop of wire in the form of a circle centre O and of radius 0.3 m, is fixed in a vertical plane. A bead of mass 0.5 kg is threaded on the wire and projected with speed u ms^{-1} from the lowest point of the wire so that it comes to instantaneous rest at a height of 0.1 m above the level of O. Find

(i) the value of u,

(ii) the reaction of the wire on the particle when the particle is level with O.

12 One end of a light inextensible string of length $2a$ is attached to a fixed point O. A particle of mass m is attached to the other end and moves in complete circles,

centre O, in a vertical plane. Its speed at the lowest point of the wire is $6\sqrt{ga}$.
Find

(a) the square of its least speed,

(b) the greatest tension in the string.

13

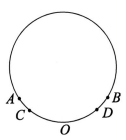

The diagram shows a vertical cross-section of a fixed circular cylinder with radius a; the point A is on the same horizontal level as the point B; the point C is on the same horizontal level as the point D and O is the lowest point of the arc $ACDB$.

(a) Iestyn has to set up a mathematical model describing the motion of a particle moving on the inside of the cylinder. He sets up a model in which a particle P released from rest at the point A reaches the point B and then returns to A and the cycle then repeats itself.

   (i) State two physical assumptions that have been made to give this model.

   (ii) Where is the force acting on P perpendicular to its velocity?

   (iii) Is the velocity of P at C equal to that at D?

   (iv) Given that A is at a height $\dfrac{a}{4}$ above O what is the speed of P at O which would be predicted by this model?

(b) Iestyn then uses the model to predict what happens when a particle is projected horizontally from the lowest point of the wire with speed u.
   Find the condition that u would have to satisfy in order that the particle goes completely round the cylinder.

14 A particle is suspended from a fixed point A by a light inelastic string of length a. Find the speed with which it must be projected horizontally from its lowest point in order that it should pass through A.

15 A bead sliding on a fixed vertical smooth circular hoop of radius a has speed V at the lowest point. Prove that the bead makes complete revolutions if $V^2 > 4ag$ and that the force exerted by the hoop on the bead is always radially inwards for $V^2 > 5ag$. If the greatest speed is $\sqrt{7}$ times the lowest speed show that

$$V = \sqrt{\frac{14ag}{3}}.$$

Find the position of the bead when the force between it and the hoop vanishes.

16

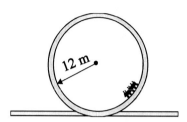

The diagram shows a roller coaster track, the circular part of which has a radius of 12 m. The roller coaster is to be designed so that the force towards the centre of the track exerted on a passsenger by her seat at the highest point is at least half her weight.

(a) Find the minimum speed at the top of the track.

(b) Find the minimum speed at the lowest point of the track.

(c) State clearly two modelling assumptions that you make.

17

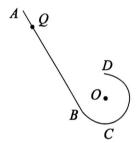

The diagram shows a vertical section of a part of the track of a fairground ride. The part AB is straight and inclined at an angle of 45° to the horizontal. The part BCD is an arc of a circle of radius a and centre O. The point C is the lowest point of the circle, D is the highest point and CD is vertical. The angle $B\hat{O}C$ is 45° so that AB is a tangent to the arc of the circle at B.

A passenger car (which is to be modelled as a particle P of mass m) is released from rest at a point Q on AB at a height $3a$ above C.

Given that the track is smooth

(a) find the reaction of the track on P when it reaches C,

(b) show that, when it is between C and D and the angle $C\hat{O}P$ is θ, the reaction of the track on P is $mg\,(4 + 3\cos\theta)$.

18   A smooth wire, on which a small bead B of mass m is threaded, is formed into a circle of radius a and fixed in a vertical plane. The bead is projected from the lowest point of the circle with speed $\sqrt{8ga}$. Show that, when the direction of motion of B has turned through an acute angle θ, the square of its speed is $6ag + 2ag\cos\theta$.

Find, in terms of m, g and θ, the reaction of the wire on the bead.

19   A banked corner of a racing track can be regarded as a circle of radius r and the gradient of the track is such that a car travelling at speed u has no tendency to side slip. Find the relationship between α, r and u.

Show that the coefficient of friction necessary to prevent sideslip at a speed $v > u$ must be at least $\dfrac{(v^2 - u^2)\sin\alpha\cos\alpha}{v^2\sin^2\alpha + u^2\cos^2\alpha}$.

20   A particle P is attached to one end of a light inextensible string of length a whose other end is attached to a fixed point O. Initially the particle is in equilibrium, suspended from O, at the point B and it is then projected horizontally with speed u from B. The particle initially moves in a circle but at a particular point of its path the string becomes slack and the particle then moves in a parabolic path which passes through B. Find the angle between the string and the upward vertical when the string becomes slack and also determine u.

21   A particle is suspended from a fixed point O by a light inelastic string of length a. The particle is projected horizontally, in the vertical plane containing the string, with speed u and the string becomes slack when it makes an angle α with the upward vertical. Find u^2 in terms of a, g and α.

Given that the particle subsequently passes through O, find the value of $\cos\alpha$.

22

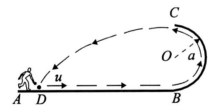

The diagram shows a vertical section ABC of a smooth surface. AB is horizontal and BC is a semicircular arc of radius a, whose centre O is at a distance a vertically above B. The surface is used in a game where a small ball P of mass m is projected with speed u towards B from a point D on AB. Subsequently it moves along the arc BC, leaving BC at C. It then moves under gravity until it first hits AB at D.

(a) Find, in terms of m, u, g, a and θ the reaction of BC on P when OP is inclined at an angle θ to the downward vertical.

(b) Find u so that $BD = 3a$.

(c) Find the smallest possible value of BD.

State two modelling assumptions that you have made.

23   A circular bend of radius r is banked at an angle α such that the maximum speed at which a car can travel around it without skidding is v. If the coefficient of friction between the wheels and the road is μ $(= \tan \lambda)$, show that this maximum speed is given by $v^2 = rg \tan (\alpha + \lambda)$.

Chapter 5

General Equilibrium of a Rigid Body

After working through this chapter, you should

- Be able to draw diagrams showing forces acting on rigid bodies including normal contact forces and friction.
- Be able to solve simple problems involving a rigid body in equilibrium under several coplanar forces.

5.1 Conditions for equilibrium

If a rigid body is in equilibrium under the action of a system of coplanar forces, then the forces satisfy the following conditions:-

(a) the sum of the forces is zero,

(b) the forces have zero moment about any point of the system.

Equivalently, the total clockwise moment is equal to the total anticlockwise moment.

For condition (a), it is often more convenient to resolve all the forces in two mutually perpendicular directions. Usually, these will be horizontal and vertical, or parallel and perpendicular to an incline plane. This gives us two independent equation. A third independent equation is obtained by taking moments about a convenient point so as to eliminate as many as possible of the unknown quantities that are not required. You can obtain two or three equations by taking moments about two or three points but you should remember that you can only get three independent equations.

In problems involving frictions, when equilibrium is about to be broken by slipping, the friction is limiting at the point of contact at which slipping is likely to occur. If the body is not on the point of moving, friction is not at its maximum possible value.

When solving problems, it is important to interpret the information given and draw a clear diagram. Mark on the diagram all the forces acting on the body and indicate clearly the direction of these forces. Sometimes it is not vital to know the direction of action of a particular force because a negative answer in the solution will indicate that the direction of the force is opposite to that indicated in the diagram.

Example 5.1

A loft door AB of length 1m and mass 5 kg is propped open at $60°$ to the horizontal by means of a strut BC. BC is of length 1 m and mass 2 kg. Find the thrust of the strut.

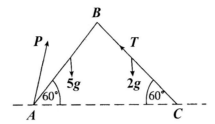

The first step is to draw a diagram showing all the forces.

T is the thrust of the strut.

P is the contact force at the hinge; its direction is unknown. If we take moments at A, P will not feature in the equation and we will only have one unknown T.

The triangle ABC is equilateral.

Taking moments about A,

$$5g \times \frac{1}{2}\cos 60° + 2g \times \left(1 - \frac{1}{2}\cos 60°\right) = T \times 1\sin 60°$$

which gives $\quad T = \dfrac{11g}{2\sqrt{3}} = 31.12$ N

Exercises 5.1

1. A uniform rod AB of mass 10 kg and length 2 m is freely hinged at A to a vertical wall. A force P is applied at B at an angle θ to AB to keep the rod in equilibrium. When in equilibrium AB makes an angle α above the horizontal. Forces X and Y are the horizontal and vertical components of the reaction at the hinge. Calculate the magnitude of P, X and Y when
   (a) $\theta = 90°, \alpha = 0°$
   (b) $\theta = 45°, \alpha = 0°$
   (c) $\theta = 30°, \alpha = 60°$

2. A uniform rod AB of mass 5 kg and length 4 m is freely hinged at A to a vertical wall. A force P applied at B at an angle θ to AB keeps the rod in equilibrium. When in equilibrium, AB makes an angle α above the horizontal. R is the reaction at the hinged which makes an angle β with the wall. Find the magnitude of the forces P and R and the size of angle β when
   (a) $\theta = 60°, \alpha = 0°$
   (b) $\theta = 60°, \alpha = 30°$
   (c) $\theta = 30°, \alpha = -45°$

3. A uniform rod AB of mass 8 kg has its lower end A in contact with a rough horizontal floor. The coefficient of friction between the rod and the floor is μ. A string is attached to end B and keeps the rod in equilibrium at an angle α with the horizontal when the string makes an angle β with the rod. Calculate the tension in the string, the normal reaction and the frictional force at A when
    (a) $\alpha = 30°, \beta = 90°$
    (b) $\alpha = 45°, \beta = 60°$
    (c) $\alpha = 60°, \beta = 30°$

4. A uniform horizontal rod AB of length 3 m and mass 20 kg is freely hinged at A to a vertical wall. The end B is attached by means of a light inextensible rope inclined at 30° to the horizontal to a point of the wall above A. A mass of 30 kg is suspended from B. Calculate the tension in the rope.
    The rope breaks when the tension exceeds $200g$ N. Calculate the largest distance from A at which an additional mass of 135 kg can be attached, to the rod AB.

5. A uniform rod AB of length 4 m and mass 5 kg is hinged freely to a vertical wall at A and has a mass of 8 kg suspended from the end B. The rod is kept in a horizontal position by a light inextensible rope CD attached to the midpoint C of the rod and a point D on the wall 1.5 m above A. Find the tension in the rope and the magnitude and direction of the force at the hinge.

6. A heavy uniform metal beam AB, 4 m long and of mass 200 kg is lifted onto a truck by means of a chain attached to end B of the beam. End A rests on rough horizontal ground. The chain passes over a pulley C fixed above the truck. The beam and chain are in the same vertical plane. The system is in equilibrium when the beam makes an angle of 25° with the ground and angle ABC is 135°. Find
    (a) the tension in the chain,
    (b) the magnitude and direction of the reaction between the beam and the ground.

7. A uniform straight rod AB has its centre of gravity at C. The rod has mass 10 kg. The rod is acted upon by a force of $20g$ N vertically upwards at end B, by a force of $10g$ N vertically downwards at end A, and by horizontal forces at B and C such that rod AB is in equilibrium inclined at an angle 30° to the horizontal with end B higher than end A. Show that the horizontal forces at B and C are equal in magnitude and find this magnitude.

5.2   Ladder problems

These are problems involving a ladder in equilibrium with its foot on the ground and its top resting against a wall. The wall or the ground may be rough or smooth and the ground may not be horizontal nor the wall vertical.

When a ladder rests against a smooth surface, there will only be a normal reaction at the point of contact perpendicular to the surface. When the surface is rough, there will also be a frictional force opposing motion.

Example 5.2

A ladder 10m long rests on rough horizontal ground against a smooth vertical wall and is inclined at an angle θ to the horizontal where $\sin\theta = \dfrac{4}{5}$. The mass of the ladder is 15 kg and its centre of mass is 4m from the lower end. A man of mass 75 kg stands on the ladder 8 m from the lower end. Find the friction force at the ground.

Draw a clear diagram showing all the forces.

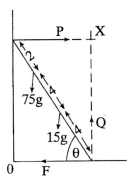

P and Q are the normal contact force from the wall and the ground. F is the friction force at the lower end of the ladder; it acts to the left as the ladder will have the tendency to slip to the right. To eliminate P and Q, take moments about X.

$$F \times 10\sin\theta = 75g \times 8\cos\theta + 15g \times 4\cos\theta$$

Substituting $\sin\theta = \dfrac{4}{5}, \cos\theta = \dfrac{3}{5}$,

$$F = 485.1 \text{ N}$$

The friction force is 485.1 N.

The remaining force on the ladder, if required, could most simply be found by resolving horizontally and vertically.

Resolving horizontally

$$P - F = 0$$
$$P = 485.1 \text{ N.}$$

Resolving vertically

$$Q - 75g - 15g = 0$$

$$Q = 882 \text{ N}$$

Also, for equilibrium to be possible, the coefficient of friction between the ladder and the ground must not less than $\dfrac{F}{Q}$, which equals 0.55.

Sometimes, it is easier to take moments about more than one point. Remember, however, that there are only three independent equations.

Example 5.3

A uniform rod AB of length 2 m and mass 5 kg has its end A resting on rough ground. It is supported at 60° to the horizontal by a string attached to its upper end B. In the position of equilibrium, the string is at right angles to AB. Calculate the tension in the string, the friction and the normal forces at A.

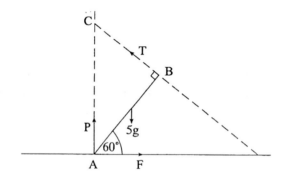

Let the tension in the string be T N, the friction F N and the normal reaction at A to be P N.

To eliminate P and F, take moments about A.

$$T \times 2 \sin 60° = 5g \times 1 \cos 60°$$

$$T = \frac{5\sqrt{3}}{6} g \text{ N.}$$

P and F may be found by resolving horizontally and vertically. Alternatively, taking moments about C will eliminate T and P.

$$F \times 2 \sec 30° = 5g \times 1 \cos 60°$$

$$F = \frac{5\sqrt{3}}{8} g \text{ N.}$$

Taking moments about D eliminates T and F.

$$P \times 2 \sec 60° = 5g (\sec 60° - 1 \cos 60°)$$

$$P = \frac{35}{8} g \text{ N.}$$

Exercises 5.2

1. A uniform ladder of mass 20 kg and length $2l$ m rests in limiting equilibrium with its upper end against a smooth vertical wall and its lower end on a rough horizontal floor. The coefficient of friction between the ladder and the floor is μ. The ladder is inclined at an angle of 75° to the horizontal.

   Calculate the normal reaction at the wall, the normal reaction and the friction force at the ground, and the value of μ.

2. A uniform ladder of mass m kg and length $2l$ m rests in limiting equilibrium with its upper end against a rough vertical wall and its lower end against a rough horizontal floor. The coefficient of friction between the ladder and the wall is $\dfrac{1}{5}$ and that between the ladder and the floor is $\dfrac{1}{3}$. The ladder makes an angle θ with the floor. Calculate the normal reactions at the wall and the floor in terms of m, g and θ.

3. A uniform ladder 8 m long, and of mass 30 kg rests with its top against a smooth vertical wall and its foot on rough ground 2 m from the wall. Find the normal and friction forces at the foot of the ladder.

4. The foot of a uniform 30 kg ladder is on rough horizontal ground with its top resting against a smooth vertical wall. The ladder is in limiting equilibrium and makes an angle of 60° with the horizontal. Find the coefficient of friction.

   If a man of mass 60 kg stands three-quarters of the way up the ladder, find the smallest horizontal force that needs to be applied to the foot of the ladder to keep it in equilibrium.

5. One end of a uniform ladder of weight W rests on a rough wall, the other end rests on rough horizontal ground. When in limiting equilibrium, the ladder is inclined at an angle θ to the vertical. The coefficient of friction between the ladder and the wall is μ and the coefficient of friction between the ladder and the ground is μ'.

   Show that

   $$\tan\theta = \frac{2\mu'}{1\mu\mu'}.$$

6. A uniform ladder of mass 50 kg rests with its upper end in contact with a smooth vertical wall and its lower end in contact with smooth horizontal ground. The ladder is being prevented from slipping by a horizontal force exerted by an inextensible string fixed to its lower end. If the breaking tension of the string is $12.5g$ N, calculate the greatest possible inclination of the ladder to the horizontal.

7. A uniform ladder of mass 8 kg rests in equilibrium with its base on a smooth horizontal floor and its top against a smooth vertical wall. The base of the ladder is 1 m from the wall and the top of the ladder is 2 m from the floor. The ladder is kept in equilibrium by a light inextensible string attached to the base of the ladder and to a point on the wall, vertically below the top of the ladder and 1m above the floor. Find the tension in the string.

8. A uniform ladder rests in limiting equilibrium with its top end against a smooth vertical wall and its base on a rough horizontal floor. The coefficient of friction between the ladder and the floor is μ. The ladder makes an angle θ with the floor. Show that $\tan\theta = \dfrac{1}{2\mu}$.

ANSWERS TO EXERCISES

<u>Exercises 1.1</u>

1. $x = ae^{3t} + be^{-3t}$

2. $x = ae^{t} + be^{2t}$

3. $x = e^{4t}(a\cos t + b\sin t)$

4. $y = ae^{4x} + be^{2x}$

5. $y = e^{-4x}(a\cos 8x + b\sin 8x)$

6. $x = ae^{\frac{4t}{3}} + be^{\frac{t}{2}}$

7. $x = a\cos 5t + b\sin 5t$

8. $y = 3\cos 4x$

9. $x = 2e^{2t}\cos 4t$

10. $x = 12e^{-2t} - 7e^{-5t}$

11. $y = \frac{1}{5}e^{4(\pi-x)}\sin 5x$

12. $x = 3e^{3t} + 2e^{-2t}$

13. $y = e^{-4x}(2\cos 2x + 6\sin 2x)$

<u>Exercises 1.2</u>

1. $x = 2 + ae^{3t} + be^{2t}$

2. $x = 2t + 3 + ae^{5t} + be^{t}$

3. $x = 2 + e^{-5t}(a\cos t + b\sin t)$

4. $x = 3t - 4 + e^{-t}(a\cos 3t + b\sin 3t)$

5. $y = 3x + 1 + ae^{-8x} + be^{-3x}$

6. $y = \frac{1}{4}x + x^2 + a + be^{-4x}$

7. $x = 3 + \frac{9}{2}e^{2t} + \frac{1}{2}e^{-10t}$

8. $x = 4 + 3e^{-2t}\cos 4t$

9. $y = 3x + 4 + xe^{-x}$

10. $y = 4 + 3e^{-2x}\cos 4x$

<u>Miscellaneous Exercises 1</u>

1. $y = 3x + 1 + e^{-x}(A\cos 3x + B\sin 3x)$

2. $y = 3 + Ae^{-3x} + Be^{-4x}$

3. (a) $x = \frac{k}{36} + Ae^{-3t} + Be^{-12t}$, $x = \frac{k}{36} - \frac{k}{27}e^{-3t} + \frac{k}{108}e^{-12t}$

  (b) $N - 3x - y$, $\dfrac{dx}{dt} = 4y$, $k = 12N$, $\dfrac{N}{3}$

4. (a) $x = e^{-2t}(A\cos 2t + B\sin 2t)$

(b) $\dfrac{dk}{dt} = I,$ $\quad\dfrac{dI}{dt} = -8k - 4I,$ $\quad k \to 0$ as $t \to \infty$

5. $\quad p = 2 + e^{-t}(0.5\cos 4t + 0.125\sin 4t)$

    (i) $\quad 2,$ (ii) $\quad 2 - 0.5e^{-\frac{\pi}{4}},$ $\quad t = \dfrac{\pi}{4}$

6. (a) $\quad y = 4x + 8 - e^{3x} - 2e^{x}$

   (b) $\quad y = e^{2x}(5\cos x - 11\sin x)$

   (c) $\quad y = e^{2x}(5 - 11x)$

7. $\quad x = \dfrac{1}{2}\left(a - \dfrac{b}{4}\right)e^{4t} + \dfrac{1}{2}\left(a + \dfrac{b}{4}\right)e^{-4t},$ $\quad 2x_0 > y_0$

Exercises 2.1

1. $\quad \sqrt{20}\ \text{ms}^{-1}$

2. $\quad 1.61\ \text{m}$

3. $\quad \sqrt{\dfrac{3}{x} - 3},\quad x = 1$

4. $\quad \dfrac{4}{x},\quad 2\sqrt{1 + 2t}$

5. $\quad 5 + x,\quad -5 + 5e^{t}$

6. $\quad e^{x},\quad \ln\left(\dfrac{2}{1 - 2t}\right)$

7. $\quad 2x^{\frac{3}{4}},\quad \dfrac{t^{4}}{16}$

8. $\quad \dfrac{\sqrt{3}}{2}\ \text{s}$

9. $\quad 50\ \text{km}$

Exercises 2.2

1. $\quad -\dfrac{5}{6}e^{-6t} + \dfrac{23}{6}$

2. $\quad (3x + 15)^{\frac{1}{3}}$

3. $\quad 2e^{-2},\quad 2e^{2} - 2$

4. $\quad \dfrac{16t}{8t + 1}$

5. $\quad t = 2\ \text{s},\quad \dfrac{8}{3}\ \text{m}$

6. $\quad 60\ \text{m}$

Exercises 2.3

1. $\dfrac{1}{4}\ln 10$ s

2. 0.96 s

3. $48\ln 2$ m

4. $1000\ln\dfrac{250}{169}$ m

5. $\dfrac{F}{mk}$, $\dfrac{\ln 4}{k}$

6. 3.12 ms^{-1},　0.91 m

7. $1.25\tan^{-1}4$ s

Miscellaneous Exercises 2

1. (a) $\dfrac{dv}{dt}=-0.1V^{2}$, $\dfrac{10(12-V)}{12V}$

   (b) takes an infinite time to come to rest,
       any resistance which does not vanish for $v=0$

2. (a) (i) $\dfrac{dv}{dt}=-4v^{n+1}$, 　(ii) 　$\dfrac{u}{\left(1+4ntu^{n}\right)^{\frac{1}{n}}}$

   (b) (i) $\dfrac{u}{\left(1+8xu^{2}\right)^{\frac{1}{2}}}$, 　(ii) 　$\dfrac{1.2u^{5}}{\left(1+8xu^{2}\right)^{\frac{5}{2}}}$

3. (a) 8, 　(b) 　6150 W, 　(c) 　1.47 km

4. $\dfrac{9.8}{k}\left(e^{-kt}-1\right)+30e^{-kt}$.　For $t=2$ s, $v=-0.01$, 　1.92 N

5. 7.8125 s, 　99.8 m

6. (i) $\ln 2$ s, 　(ii) 2 m

7. (a) (i) $\sqrt{u^{2}-2g(x-b)}$, (ii) stops when $x=\dfrac{u^{2}+2gb}{2g}$ and returns to earth

   (b) (i) $\sqrt{u^{2}+\dfrac{2k}{x}-\dfrac{2k}{b}}$, 　(ii) returns to earth, 　(iii) escapes to infinity

9. $U^{2}=\dfrac{g}{k}\left(1-e^{-2kH}\right)$

10. $5t+50\left(e^{\frac{-t}{10}}-1\right)$

11. $6gt-36g\left(1-e^{-\frac{t}{6}}\right)$

12. (a) (i) $n\sqrt{\dfrac{2}{5}}$, 　(ii) $-3a$

    (b) (i) $2n$ 　(ii) $p<\dfrac{1}{3}$

Exercises 3.1

1. π s

2.   0.5 m, 0.3 m

3. $\dfrac{1}{\pi}$ ms^{-1}

4. $\dfrac{5}{3\pi}$ m

5.   5 m, π s

6.   5 m,   20 ms^{-1}

7.   0.4 m

8. $2\sqrt{5}$ m $\dfrac{2\pi}{3}$ s

9.   63.7 Hz

10.   0.63 ms^{-1} to 1.57 ms^{-1}

11.   0.22 s, 0.12 s

12. $3\sin\left(\dfrac{\pi}{12}\right)$ m

13.   0.057

14.   6.48 am

15.   12.32 am and 8.18 pm

16. $\dfrac{0.2\pi}{3}$ ms^{-1}, $\dfrac{0.2\pi^2}{9}$ ms^{-2}

17.   4.2 N, 3.6 N

18.   0.06 m

19. $\dfrac{35}{\pi}$ Hz

20.   Does not slip

21. 9.9×10^{-4} m

22.   2 m, $\dfrac{2\pi}{\sqrt{5}}$ s, $x = 1$ m

Exercises 3.2

1. (a) 0.13 s,   (b)   0.17 s

2. $x = -0.4\sin 2t$ m, $v = -0.8\cos 2t$ ms^{-1}

3.   1.13 s

4. (a) 0.13 s,   (b)   0.17 s

5.   1.13 s

6. (a) $\dfrac{\pi}{16}$ s,   (b) 0.23 s

7.   0.2 m, 0.05 s

134

8.   0.25 s

9.   1.10 s,   0.2 m

10.   0.13

11.   0.77 s

12. 0.24 ms^{-1},   0.16 s

13. 1.4 ms^{-1}

Exercises 3.3

1. $0.52e^{-12t} - 0.48e^{-13t}$

2. $0.05e^{-4t}\sin 12t$

3. $-e^{-4t} + 0.8e^{-5t}$

4. $-0.2te^{-5t}$

5. $\dfrac{2\pi}{3}$ s

6. $\dfrac{3\pi}{20}$

7.   2.53 N

Miscellaneous Exercises 3

1.   (i)   8m,   (ii) $\dfrac{\pi}{18}$ s,   (iii) $108\sqrt{3}$ W,   (iv)   216 W

2. $\dfrac{\pi}{3}$ rads^{-1},   2 m, $\dfrac{5\pi}{6}$ rad, $\dfrac{5\pi}{3}$ ms^{-1}

3. $e^{-t}(A\cos 2t + B\sin 2t)$, $b = -\dfrac{1}{2}$, $2e^{-t}\cos 2t$

4.   (i) $\sqrt{2gx}$, $x = 0.6$, $t = \dfrac{\pi}{19.8}$,   (iv) 3.28 ms^{-1}, 0.932

5.   (i) $\dfrac{2\pi}{3}$ s, (ii) 0.057 m, (iii) $0.057\sin 5t$, (iv) 0.16 s, 3.75 N

6. $a\cos\omega t$,   (i) $\dfrac{\pi}{3\omega}$ (ii) $\dfrac{5\pi}{12\omega}$,   (iii) $4b$,   (iv) $5b$

7.   0.2 m,   2.96 N

8. $e^{-t}(0.28\cos 7t + 0.04\sin 7t)$,   0.82 m

9.   (i)   5 N,   (ii) $10(x + 0.098)$ N,   (iv) $\dfrac{\pi}{5}$ s,   (v) 0.433 ms^{-1}

    (vi)   string becomes slack during motion

10. (i) $0.6\sin\dfrac{\pi}{3}t$,   (ii)   0.5   (iii) $0.083\sin\dfrac{\pi}{3}t\cos\dfrac{\pi}{3}t$ W

11.   (i) 1.568 m,   (ii) 0.2 cos 2.5t (iii) $\dfrac{\pi}{5}$ s, (iv) $\dfrac{2\pi}{15}$ s,

$$\frac{d^2x}{dt^2} = -6.25\left(x - 0.4\sin 2t\right)$$

12.   (ii) 0.1 m, $\dfrac{\pi}{40}$ s,   (iii) 0.1 sin 20t m, 2 cos 20t ms^{-1},   (iv) $\dfrac{\pi}{60}$ s,

    (v)   Car moves away with same speed as it collides. This takes no account of
        energy loss due to collision

13.   1.5 m, 12.5 hrs, $8.5 + 1.5\cos\dfrac{4\pi}{25}t$ m,   20.27 hrs,   0.754 cm per min

14.   13 cm, π s, $\dfrac{\pi}{4}$ s

15. $\dfrac{a}{5}\cos\sqrt{\dfrac{5g}{a}}t$, $2\pi\sqrt{\dfrac{a}{5g}}$

16.   2 s, $\sqrt{10}$ m

17.   140 N,   1.67 ms^{-1}

18. $\dfrac{d^2y}{dt^2} + \dfrac{2k}{m}y = 0$, $\dfrac{a}{6}\cos\sqrt{\dfrac{2k}{m}}t$

21. $\sqrt{6}$ m

22. $\dfrac{a}{2}\left(1 + \sqrt{5}\right)$

24.   5 m, $\dfrac{8\pi}{5}$ s, $\dfrac{4\pi}{15}$ s

25. $2g + 0.6\pi^2$ N, $2g - 0.6\pi^2$ N

26. $k^2 < 1$, $k = 0.16$, $n = 2.03$

Exercises 4.1

1.   60.75 N
2.   1.3
3.   0.87 m
4.   0.83 s
5.   0.13
7.   497.4 N
8. $0.58\sqrt{\dfrac{g}{a}}$
9.   9.33 ms^{-1}
10. $\sqrt{\dfrac{5g}{3a}}$

Exercises 4.2

1. 2.3 ms^{-1}

2. 1705 N

3. 0.99 m

4. 6064 N

5. 1.65 s

6. $\sqrt{gh}$

7. $2\pi\sqrt{\dfrac{3a}{5g}}$

8. $\dfrac{5mg}{3}, \quad \dfrac{5mg}{12}, \quad \dfrac{1}{2}$

10. $mg\sin\alpha + \dfrac{mv^2}{a}\cot\alpha, \quad m\left(\dfrac{v^2}{a} - g\cos\alpha\right), \quad v^2 > ga\cos\alpha$

11. $\dfrac{11}{7}$

Exercises 4.3

1. 451 N

2. 12.5 ms^{-1}

3. $63.9°$

4. 82.8 ms^{-1}

5. $1.25 \, mg\sin\alpha$

6. 0.33

7. $8.2°$

8. $0.33, \quad 0.37$

9. $14.6°$

10. $11.9 \text{ ms}^{-1} \leq v \leq 42.7 \text{ ms}^{-1}$

Exercises 4.4

1. $\sqrt{68ag}$

2. $\sqrt{2ag}$

3. 5.65 ms^{-1}

4. 6.26 ms^{-1}

5. $2760 \text{ N}, \qquad 1290 \text{ N}$

6. 1.98 ms^{-1}

7. $\mu\omega^2 \geq 28(\sin\theta + \mu\cos\theta)$

8. $3mg \sin \theta$

9. $\dfrac{a}{3}$

10. $\sqrt{ag(2+3\pi)}$

Miscellaneous Exercises 4

1. $m(g - h\omega^2)$, $\sqrt{\dfrac{g}{h}}$,   (i) $a + \dfrac{aT}{mg}$,   (ii) $\dfrac{T}{m\Omega^2}$ $\dfrac{mga\Omega^2}{g - a\Omega^2}$

2. (a) $\sqrt{\dfrac{3ag}{2}}$, $\pi\sqrt{\dfrac{2a}{g}}$,   (b) $\dfrac{m\omega^2}{a} - mg + 3mg \cos\theta$, $2\sqrt{ag}$

3.   0.1, $90mg$

4. $mg \sin\alpha - m\ell\omega^2 \sin\alpha \cos\alpha$, $mg \cos\alpha + m\ell\omega^2 \sin^2\alpha$,

$\sqrt{\dfrac{g \sec\alpha}{\ell}}$, $\dfrac{49a}{141}$

5.   0.77,   53.7°

7. $\sqrt{\dfrac{61ga}{45}}$

8. $\dfrac{2g}{5\pi^2}$

9.   23.52 kN,   212 m

10. $\dfrac{2}{3}$, $2\sqrt{ag}$

11.   (i)   2.8   (ii)   3.27 N

12. (a) $28ag$,   (b) $19mg$

13. (a) (i) smooth cylinder, no air resistance   (ii) 0,   (iii) No,   (iv) $\sqrt{\dfrac{ag}{2}}$

(b) $u^2 \geq 5ag$

14. $\sqrt{ag(2 + \sqrt{3})}$

15.   radius to bead at $\cos^{-1} \dfrac{8}{9}$ to upward vertical

16. (a) 13.28 ms^{-1} (b)   25.43 ms^{-1}

17. (a) $7mg$

18. $3mg (2 + \cos\theta)$

20. $\dfrac{\pi}{3}$, $\sqrt{\dfrac{7ag}{2}}$

21. $ag(2 + 3\cos\alpha)$, $\dfrac{1}{\sqrt{3}}$

22. (a) $\dfrac{mu^2}{a} - 2mg + 3mg \cos\theta$,   (b) $\dfrac{5}{2}\sqrt{ag}$ (c)   4a

Exercises 5.1

1. (a) 5g N,   0,   5g N,   (b) $5g\sqrt{2}$ N,   5g N,   5g N

   (c) 5g N, $\dfrac{5g\sqrt{3}}{2}$ N, $\dfrac{25g}{2}$ N

2. (a) $\dfrac{5g}{\sqrt{3}}$ N, $\dfrac{5g}{\sqrt{3}}$ N,   30°,   (b) $\dfrac{5g}{2}$ N, $\dfrac{5g\sqrt{3}}{2}$ N,   30°

   (c) $10g\sqrt{2}$ N,   92.14 N,   113°

3. (a) $2g\sqrt{3}$ N,   11 g, $g\sqrt{3}$ N   (b) $\dfrac{8g}{3}$ N,   71.6 N,   28.4 N

   (c) 4g N,   10g N, $2g\sqrt{3}$ N

4.   80g N, $1\dfrac{1}{3}$ m

5.   35g N,   431.6 N,   51° to the vertical

6. (a) 890 N,   61° to the horizontal,   (b) 1256 N
7. $20g\sqrt{3}$ N

Exercises 5.2

1.   26.26 N,   196 N,   26.26 N,   0.134.

2. $\dfrac{5mg\cos\theta}{10\sin\theta + 2\cos\theta}$, $\dfrac{3mg\cos\theta}{6\cos\theta - 2\sin\theta}$

3.   30g N, $5g\sqrt{3}$ N

4. $\dfrac{1}{2\sqrt{3}}$, $g\sqrt{15}$ N

6. $\tan^{-1} 2$

7. $2g\sqrt{2}$ N

INDEX